METHUEN'S MONOGRAPHS

ON APPLIED PROBABILITY AND STATISTICS

General Editor: M. S. BARTLETT

THE FOUNDATIONS OF
STATISTICAL INFERENCE

Prepared Contributions

L. J. SAVAGE, *University of Michigan*
M. S. BARTLETT, *University College, London*
G. A. BARNARD, *Imperial College, London*
D. R. COX, *Birkbeck College, London*
E. S. PEARSON, *University College, London*
C. A. B. SMITH, *University College, London*

Discussion

The above and
H. RUBEN, *University of Sheffield*
I. J. GOOD, *Admiralty Research Establishment*
D. V. LINDLEY, *University College of Wales, Aberystwyth*
P. ARMITAGE, *London School of Hygiene & Tropical Medicine*
C. B. WINSTEN, *Imperial College, London*
R. SYSKI, *University of Maryland*
E. D. VAN REST, *Ministry of Supply*
G. M. JENKINS, *Imperial College, London*

The Foundations of
Statistical Inference

A Discussion

*Opened by Professor L. J. Savage
at a meeting of the Joint Statistics Seminar,
Birkbeck and Imperial Colleges,
in the University of London*

LONDON: METHUEN & CO LTD

NEW YORK: JOHN WILEY & SONS INC

First published in 1962
© 1962 *by G. A. Barnard and D. R. Cox*
Printed in Great Britain by
Spottiswoode Ballantyne & Co Ltd
London & Colchester
Catalogue No. (*Methuen*) 2/5237/11

Contents

Preface

When it became known that Professor L. J. Savage was visiting London in the summer of 1959 and was willing to speak on the applications of subjective probability to statistics, it was arranged that he should address the Joint Statistics Seminar of Birkbeck and Imperial Colleges. The present monograph is based on papers and discussion at that meeting which took place at Birkbeck College on July 27th and 28th.

The monograph is in three parts. Part I is a somewhat expanded form of Professor Savage's opening lecture. Part II gives five short invited contributions that had been prepared in advance of Professor Savage's lecture. A sixth contribution by Professor D. V. Lindley is not reproduced here, but has appeared in expanded form as a paper in the *Proceedings of the Fourth Berkeley Symposium*. The discussion recorded in Part III of the monograph is largely concerned with the issues raised in Professor Savage's lecture. In editing, the order in which the discussion took place has been slightly rearranged and one or two additional statements have been inserted.

Acknowledgements

Professor Savage's research, described in Part I, was supported by the United States Air Force through the Air Force Office of Scientific Research of the Air Research and Development Command, under Contract No. AF 49(638)-391, and by the Office of Naval Research, under Contract Nonr-2121(09). Reproduction of Part I, in whole or in part, is permitted for any purpose of the United States Government.

We are very grateful to the speakers for allowing their contributions to be included, and for their help in preparing the monograph.

G. A. BARNARD
D. R. COX

London
May 1961

PART I

Subjective Probability and Statistical Practice

LEONARD J. SAVAGE

1. Introduction

I am here to enlist your active participation in a movement with practical implications for statistical theory and applications at all levels, from the most elementary classroom to the most sophisticated research. Personal contact with so many competent and active statisticians in connection with issues that still seem liable to emotional misinterpretation when merely written is very auspicious. Nor could one possibly arrange better to stimulate and hear the criticisms and doubts that the subjectivistic contribution to statistics must answer.

My own attitude toward the movement has changed materially since I contributed to it a book called *The Foundations of Statistics* (Savage, 1954). Though this book emphasizes the merits of the concept of subjective (or personal) probability, it was not written in the anticipation of radical changes in statistical practice. The idea was, rather, that subjective probability would lead to a better justification of statistics as it was then taught and practised, without having any urgent practical consequences. However, it has since become more and more clear that the concept of subjective probability is capable of suggesting and unifying important advances in statistical practice.

It helps to emphasize at the outset that the role of subjective probability in statistics is, in a sense, to make statistics less subjective. We all know how much the activity of one who uses statistics depends on judgement, both in the planning of experiments and in the analysis of them. For example, we are often counselled by statistical theory to choose among the many operating characteristic functions that reflect the choice of an experiment and an analysis, or the choice of an analysis alone. This choice among available operating characteristics is recognized almost universally to be a subjective matter, depending on the judgement of the person, or of each person, concerned. The theory of subjective probability shows these necessarily subjective judgements to be far less arbitrary or free than they have heretofore superficially seemed, and therein lies much of the value of this concept for statistics.

I know little of the early history of subjective probability, though early references could surely be found. The earliest clear statement of the concept of subjective probability known to me is due to Borel (1924). A little more recent but more thoroughgoing was the formulation of Ramsey (1931), which is in no way obsolete. Ramsey was followed closely and independently by de Finetti (1937, 1949, 1958), who continues to explore the foundations of probability with extraordinary competence and thoroughness. Adequate formulation was also given by Koopman (1940a, b; 1941). These pioneers in the concept of subjective probability did not write as statisticians, and the application of the concept to statistics raises many questions outside the scope of their work.

There are doubtless many relatively early publications discussing the application of subjective probability to statistics, for example, those by Molina (1931) and Fry (1934). But the idea was much discouraged for several decades. The book by I. J. Good (1950) is a landmark in its statistical reawakening; see also Good (1952). In recent years, several qualified statisticians have been interested in more or less explicit applications of subjective probability (Anscombe, 1958; Hodges and Lehmann, 1952; Lindley, 1956; Wallace, 1959; Whittle, 1958). A most interesting textbook on statistics for students of business that wholeheartedly embraces subjective probability has recently been published by Robert Schlaifer (1959).

Though Sir Harold Jeffreys has not been a subjectivist, his work, exemplified by two books (Jeffreys, 1948, 1957), in common with that of subjectivists, makes serious use of Bayes's theorem. Moreover, Jeffreys's belief in the existence of canonical initial distributions (for certain situations) does not keep him from studying also arbitrary initial distributions, which are just what subjectivists need. Anyone wishing to explore subjective probability will find many valuable lessons in the two books just mentioned that do not yet seem to be available elsewhere, and much of what I shall say here is taken directly from Jeffreys.

Today's talk is not axiomatic, and mathematical rigour is not one of its objectives, though I shall of course not willfully make mathematical mistakes. It is mainly through examples that I hope to leave you more interested in, and more sanguine about, applications of subjective probability to statistical inference.

By inference I mean roughly how we find things out – whether with a view to using the new knowledge as a basis for explicit action or not – and how it comes to pass that we often acquire practically identical opinions in the light of evidence. Statistical inference is not the whole of inference but a special kind. The typical inference of the detective, historian, or conjecturing mathematician and the clever inferences of science are not statistical inferences. Still, it is hard to draw the line, and there seems to be nothing to lose and much to gain by keeping the more general concept in mind, provided we remember to give special attention to those aspects of inference that seem especially appropriate to the working statistician.

2. Subjective probability

Subjective probability refers to the opinion of a person as reflected by his real or potential behaviour. This person is idealized; unlike you and me, he never makes mistakes, never gives thirteen pence for a shilling, or makes such a combination of bets that he is sure to lose no matter what happens. Though we are not quite like that person, we wish we were, and it will be important for you to try to put yourself mentally in his place. To facilitate this identification, Good (1950) called him 'you', and I shall for the moment call him 'thou'. The probability that refers to thee is basically a probability measure in the usual sense of modern mathematics. It is a function Pr that assigns a real number to each of a reasonably large class of events A, B, . . ., including a universal event S, in such a way that if A and B have nothing in common,

$$\Pr(A \text{ or } B) = \Pr(A) + \Pr(B),$$
$$\Pr(A) \geqslant 0,$$
$$\Pr(S) = 1.$$

The extra-mathematical thing, the thing of crucial importance, is that Pr is entirely determined in a certain way by potential behaviour. Specifically, Pr(A) is such that

$$\Pr(A)/\Pr(\text{not } A) = \Pr(A)/\{1 - \Pr(A)\}$$

is the odds that thou wouldst barely be willing to offer for A against not A.

The definition just given will not be altogether unfamiliar to you, and you will see what it is driving at. Roughly speaking, it can be shown that such a probability structure Pr, and one only, exists for every person who behaves coherently in that he is not prepared to make a combination of bets that is sure to lose (de Finetti, 1937, pp. 6–9; Savage, 1954). This assertion is not quite correct in that a coherent person may justifiably vary his odds with the size of the bet. To use this definition effectively, you should try to think in terms of bets that are rather small but worth considering. The great advantage of this definition over more rigorous ones like the one borrowed from de Finetti (1937, pp. 4–5) for use in my book (Savage, 1954) is that the one in terms of odds seems much easier to apply introspectively. Without insisting on an axiomatic exploration today, please believe that there is considerable rationale behind the concept of subjective probability in the various references cited, make an introspective effort to apply the concept to yourself, and see with me what it leads to in a few statistical examples.

The concept of subjective probability has serious defects. These can be instructively appraised by exploring the close analogy between the odds that you would offer on an event, and the price at which you would buy or sell some valuable object. Both concepts are afflicted with vagueness and temptation to dishonesty. It might be hard for you to fix with precision the odds that you would offer that a particular keg of nails meets some specified industrial standard or that the moon is covered thickly with fine dust; in the same way, it might be hard for you to specify the price at which you would sell your automobile or buy a specific piece of information about the aurora borealis. Again, if the facts about the nails or the moon should be disclosed to you, it may become even harder to say honestly what you would have bet; similarly, once highly satisfactory prices have been offered to you, it is even harder than before to say honestly what prices would have been just satisfactory.

These difficulties are real, but they must not be allowed to frighten us out of trying to use the concepts at all. We can, if we try, do quite a bit with them as they are, and we can mitigate some of their inadequacies by using common sense and ingenuity. There is the hope that distinct improvements will be made on such concepts some day, but it seems to me that they are, each in its own line, the best that we have today.

Most people tacitly accept, and I think justifiably, that the concept of (equilibrium) price cannot be altogether escaped by anyone who would think of his own or other people's economic behaviour. But statistical theory has for several decades been largely dedicated to trying, futilely, I would say, to escape altogether from the concept of acceptable odds, or subjective probability, at least where the analysis of data is concerned. In so far as we want to arrive at opinions on the basis of data, it seems inescapable that we should use, together with the data, the opinions that we had before it was gathered. And I believe that 'opinion', when analysed, is coterminal with 'odds'. We have had a slogan about letting the data speak for themselves, but when they do, they tell us only how to modify our opinions, not what opinion is justifiable. If my statement of these general principles is somewhat dogmatic and abrupt, it is because I trust that examples will show you better than abstract arguments how the ingenious attempts to build a statistical theory without subjective probability have fallen short and how the concept of subjective probability leads to substantial improvements.

To my own mind, one of the most striking symptoms of the inadequacy of statistical theory without subjective probability is the lack of unity that such theory has had. I speak not only of such schisms as that between the adherents of R. A. Fisher and those of Neyman and Pearson, but also of the ununified, or opportunistic, structure of the theories proposed by both of these two schools.

For example, according to the Neyman-Pearson school there are many different virtues that a system of confidence intervals might have. A user of statistics is supposed to try to achieve as many of these as possible, and then to choose among them when there is conflict.

Typically, this theory leaves the user of statistics with a wide range of choices. He is supposed to survey the available operating character-istics and choose the one that he likes best among those that are at all reasonable (that is, admissible or nearly so). This choice is frankly subjective, but for certain historical reasons, the dominant school of statisticians has not seen that the idea of subjective probability makes the choice easier and more systematic than it would at first sight seem to be.

The recommendations of Fisher (1956) present a different kind of fragmentation. He counsels us to do one thing when we know 'nothing', a state of knowledge difficult, really impossible, to define, and to do another when initial probabilities, in some nonsubjectivis-tic sense, permit application of Bayes's theorem. Even when we know 'nothing', Fisher does not present us with a unified method, but tells us to use fiducial probability, when the 'fiducial argument', the mean-ing of which is still a little hazy, applies, and to do something quite different when it does not apply.

The fragmentation presented by these theories suggests, though it does not prove, that something important is missing, and the appli-cation of subjective probability does make for unity. The subjectivist too will of course exploit the advantages of special situations, but he sees these not isolated as islands but as interesting regions merging with the rest of the mainland.

It is sometimes alleged as a criticism of the concept of subjective probability that science must be objective, that right reason must lead from given evidence to one and only one right conclusion. This line of thinking does not appear to be valid, fruitful or practical; see Bridgman (1940). Though it has, I think it fair to say, been expressed in some form by adherents of the school of Neyman and Pearson, it is certainly not essential to that school, which for the most part freely admits that the reaction to an experiment depends on subjective factors, like choice among operating characteristics. It seems to me that such 'objectivity' as we enjoy in practice stems from the tendency of diverse opinions to converge toward one another under the weight of evidence. It must be emphasized that this convergence is non-uniform, so it cannot be pretended that only a small sphere of opinions is left open after the accumulation of weighty evidence. In particular,

I believe R. A. Fisher is mistaken when he argues thus: 'This property of increasingly large samples has been sometimes put forward as a reason for accepting the postulate of knowledge *a priori*. It appears, however, more natural to infer from it that it should be possible to draw valid conclusions from the data alone, and without *a priori* assumptions' (Fisher, 1934, p. 287).

It has sometimes been contended that there are two different kinds of statistical theory, one appropriate to economic contexts and another to pure science; see, for example, Fisher (1955). In my own opinion, this dualistic view is incorrect. At any rate, the applications of subjective probability to be discussed today are equally available to economic and scientific applications of statistics. Except that subjective probability is defined as an economic concept, in terms of choice among gambles, this talk will scarcely refer explicitly to decision, loss, or other economic concepts. When subjective probability is taken seriously these other concepts, though they remain important, become relatively uninteresting, because in principle the solution of every decision problem is simply to maximize expected income with respect to the subjective probability that applies at the moment of making the decision. This leaves us free, at least in today's talk, to emphasize the calculation of posterior, or final, probabilities, though in more advanced applications the quality of certain approximations would have to be judged partly on the basis of possible losses.

3. Bayes's theorem and the likelihood principle

Write Bayes's theorem somewhat informally thus:

$$\Pr(\lambda \,|\, x) \;\propto\; \Pr(x \,|\, \lambda)\,\Pr(\lambda). \tag{1}$$

In words, the probability that the unknown parameter has the value λ given the datum x is proportional to the product of the probability of observing x given λ multiplied by the initial probability of λ. 'Proportionality' here means proportionality in λ regarding x as fixed; if a different datum x' were observed, there would typically be a different constant of proportionality. As is familiar to you all, the various probabilities referred to can also be interpreted as probability densities where necessary; a more general formula can of course be written, but this one seems to have mnemonic value.

It is helpful to notice that in usual applications of statistics the probability of x given λ tends to have a quality that might cautiously be called 'objectivity'. For example, everyone concerned with the experiment may be agreed that x is normally distributed around λ with unit variance, or that x is a Poisson variable with mean λ, or that x is normally distributed with mean μ and variance σ^2, the parameter λ in the last example consisting of the pair (μ, σ^2). These probabilities are not really objective; they are expressions of opinions. In practice, they are seldom even taken seriously as realistic opinions by experienced statisticians, but are regarded as rather rough practical ways to get on with the problem until more realistic assumptions prove necessary. For example, if x is supposed to be 15 normally distributed physical measurements, there will probably be serious talk by all concerned about a spurious, or outlying, observation if the largest reading is separated from the second largest by as much as the second largest is from the least. This means that all concerned have (and therefore presumably always had latent) some doubts about the rigorous normality of the sample. Similarly, a sample in which the magnitude of the readings is nearly perfectly correlated with the order in which they were taken is sure to raise eyebrows. In short, simple models do not often fully represent our opinions about the possible outcomes of an experiment. Useful though such models are, the danger of accepting them literally cannot be overemphasized.

In contrast with the conditional probability of x given λ, the probability of λ itself is usually conspicuously personal and vague. In principle, anyone can, by asking himself how he would bet, elicit his own subjective probability distribution for the velocity of neon light in beer. But no one is really prepared to do so with much precision, and still less is close agreement from person to person to be expected. It is largely because of these difficulties that Bayes's theorem has so long been regarded as useless by most modern statisticians. Not only are these difficulties often surmountable, but, in my experience, whenever an experiment justifies a conclusion the justification can always be given in terms of Bayes's theorem.

In view of (1), if the initial probability of λ is ill-defined or not agreed upon, the same must be true of the final probability of λ, that is, the probability of λ given x. Nonetheless, there is an important practical sense in which the probability of λ given x may be much more precise and much better agreed upon than the initial probability of λ, as will be illustrated in the next section.

According to Bayes's theorem, $\Pr(x|\lambda)$, considered as a function of λ, constitutes the entire evidence of the experiment, that is, it tells all that the experiment has to tell. More fully and more precisely, if y is the datum of some other experiment, and if it happens that $\Pr(x|\lambda)$ and $\Pr(y|\lambda)$ are proportional functions of λ (that is, constant multiples of each other), then each of the two data x and y have exactly the same thing to say about the values of λ. For example, the probability of seeing 6 red-eyed flies in a randomly drawn sample of 100 is proportional to $\lambda^6(1-\lambda)^{94}$, where λ is the frequency of red-eyed flies in the population, whether the experiment consisted in counting the number of red-eyed flies in a random sample of 100, or of sampling flies at random until 6 with red eyes are observed, or countless other sequential variations of these experiments. I, and others, call this important principle the likelihood principle. The function $\Pr(x|\lambda)$ – rather this function together with all others that result from it by multiplication by a positive constant – is called the likelihood.

The likelihood principle flows directly from Bayes's theorem and the concept of subjective probability, and it is to my mind a good example of the fertility of these ideas. The principle was, however, first emphasized to statisticians by Barnard (1947b) and Fisher (1956), on other grounds. It seems to command more and more assent the more you think about it, criticize it, and seek counterexamples against it.

The likelihood principle is, however, in conflict with many historically important concepts of statistics. For example, whether a test (or an estimate) is unbiased depends not on the likelihood alone, but rather on $\Pr(x|\lambda)$ considered as a function of x as well as a function of λ. Similarly with the concepts of significance or confidence level. For instance, it has been widely believed that the import of such a datum as 6 red-eyed flies out of 100 depends on whether the experiment was designed to observe 100 flies or designed to observe 6 red-eyed flies. An estimate unbiased for either of these experiments is biased for the other, and there is a considerable literature on unbiased estimates for sequential observation of Bernoullian data, to which I

B

myself have contributed (Blackwell, 1947; DeGroot, 1959; Girshick *et al.*, 1946; Savage, 1947). In view of the likelihood principle, all of these classical statistical ideas come under new scrutiny, and must, I believe, be abandoned or seriously modified.

The principle has important implications in connection with optional stopping. Suppose the experimenter admitted that he had seen 6 red-eyed flies in 100 and had then stopped because he felt that he had thereby accumulated enough data to overthrow some popular theory that there should be about 1 per cent red-eyed flies. Does this affect the interpretation of 6 out of 100? Statistical tradition emphasizes, in connection with this question, that if the sequential properties of his experimental programme are ignored, the persistent experimenter can arrive at data that nominally reject any null hypothesis at any significance level, when the null hypothesis is in fact true. Such a rejection is therefore no real evidence against the null hypothesis. These truths are usually misinterpreted to suggest that the data of such a persistent experimenter are worthless or at least need special interpretation; see, for example, Anscombe (1954), Feller (1940), Robbins (1952). The likelihood principle, however, affirms that the experimenter's intention to persist does not change the import of his experience. The true moral of the facts about optional stopping is that significance level is not really a good guide to 'level of significance' in the sense of 'degree of import', for the degree of import does depend on the likelihood alone, a theme to which I must return later in the lecture.

There is a class of actuarial problems of considerable theoretical, and perhaps also practical, interest that promises to be greatly simplified by systematic application of the likelihood principle. Here is an example. Children come into a clinic for observation at various time intervals after the onset of a serious disease and remain under observation until they are either withdrawn from the clinic, say by arbitrary action of their parents, or until they die, or until they survive for five years after the onset of the disease.

It is desired to estimate the probability of surviving for five years. In practice this is messy data, because there is a more than justifiable suspicion that the moment when children are brought to the clinic or withdrawn from it has some correlation with the prognosis, but even if this practical point is set aside, the formal problem that remains is still a complicated one. There has been considerable study of such problems based on objectivistic statistical ideas like unbiasedness and confidence intervals, and depending on various stochastic models of the mechanism that brings subjects into the study and withdraws them from it. Recent key references are the papers of Elveback (1958) and Kaplan and Meier (1958). According to the likelihood principle, however, these mechanisms have nothing to do with the import of the data for the pressure of mortality and, in particular, for the probability of surviving for five years. With this hint, new progress on the problem is to be expected and many dead ends are recognized.

To see how the likelihood principle works on a problem of the type envisaged in the preceding paragraphs, divide the five-year interval into short intervals, and suppose it is known that of x_i children who had survived to the beginning of the ith interval, y_i survived throughout that interval. If p_i is the probability that a child who survives to the ith interval will survive through it, then $p = \Pi p_i$ is the probability of five-year survival. Irrespective of any model that might be proposed to account for the x_i, say in terms of parameters ξ,

$$\Pr(x_1,\ldots; y_1,\ldots \,|\, p_1,\ldots; \xi)$$
$$= \Pr(x_1 \,|\, \xi)\,\Pr(y_1 \,|\, p_1, x_1)\,\Pr(x_2 \,|\, x_1, \xi)\,\Pr(y_2 \,|\, p_2, x_2)\ldots$$
$$= f(x_1,\ldots; \xi)\,\Pi p_i^{y_i}(1-p_i)^{x_i-y_i}.$$

The function f is irrelevant to the likelihood, so that only the observed x_i, not the mechanism which produced them, enters into the likelihood.

The concept of ancillary statistic, introduced by Fisher, has been difficult to grasp and to define precisely – see, for example, Cox (1958a) – but the likelihood principle seems to provide the key. A typical important instance of an ancillary statistic is this. If x_i and y_i are both from a random source, say independent sample pairs from a joint normal distribution, and the problem is to study the regression of y on x, then it is, everyone seems to agree, legitimate to make all inferences as though the x_i were not random and the original experimental plan had been to sample the y_i exactly at these x_i. The x_i are here called an ancillary statistic, and the likelihood principle does indeed make it clear that the mechanism that happened to select the x_i is of no relevance to inferences about the regression coefficient. Actually, it is tacit in this argument that perfect knowledge of the distribution from which the x_i were sampled would be of no use (or, more realistically, of little use) in drawing conclusions about the regression coefficient. This is a subjective matter and can therefore vary from problem to problem and person to person. One might, for example, have some strong special reason to believe that if the x_i are broadly (or narrowly) distributed the regression coefficient is likely to be large.

The likelihood principle always supports the appealing conclusions that have been based on ancillary statistics. But the likelihood principle leads to the simplifications almost automatically, whereas ancillary statistics are discovered only by ingenuity and insight. An important reason for this is that one problem can have many ancillary statistics on a par with each other. For a striking, if academic, example, suppose x and y are normal about 0 with variance 1 and correlation ρ. Then x and y are each by themselves irrelevant to ρ, and each is an ancillary statistic for the total observation (x, y) by any criterion known to me. Inclusion of several pairs (x_i, y_i), rather than one only, makes no essential difference.

4. Precise measurement

One of the most interesting and satisfying applications of subjective probability is that of precise measurement. This is the kind of measurement we have when the data are so incisive as to overwhelm the initial opinion, thus bringing a great variety of realistic initial opinions to practically the same conclusion. Put yourself – not an over-idealized person – into a certain statistical situation of textbook simplicity. The one I propose is humble but, for me, instructive. Whoever finds it frivolous can supply something graver: the weight of a nougat or of the earth, the melting point of a new compound, or the sex-ratio at birth in post-war Germany – a good example, because sample frequency here is so like a normal measurement of variance $\frac{1}{4}N^{-1}$.

You are holding a potato, or some other irregular object, in your hand and have need to know something about its weight. You can, in principle, elicit your own initial probability density $\alpha(\lambda)$ for the unknown weight of the potato, but in practice the self-interrogation may not work very well and you may be very vague about $\alpha(\lambda)$. There is a temptation, under these circumstances, to say that $\alpha(\lambda)$ does not exist or that you know nothing about the weight of the potato. Actually, it has proved impossible to give a satisfactory definition of the tempting expression 'know nothing'. Still more, you do know a good deal about your opinions about the weight of the potato, and these can be quite well expressed in terms of partial specifications of $\alpha(\lambda)$. If, for example, it were necessary to mail the potato without weighing it, you could put on enough postage to be reasonably sure that it would not be returned to you nor be 500 per cent overpaid.

More important, you are almost sure to have a certain kind of knowledge about $\alpha(\lambda)$, which has seldom been mentioned explicitly, but which will be very useful after you have a chance to weigh the potato on a good balance. To illustrate, suppose that you found out, as a result of some experiment, that the weight of the potato to the nearest gram was either 146 or 147 gm. Given this knowledge, you would probably be willing to accept odds only slightly more favourable than one-to-one in favour of either of the two possibilities, 146 gm or 147 gm. This may be interpreted to mean that, for you, the average value of $\alpha(\lambda)$ near 146 is almost the same as its average value near 147. Continuing along this line, you might arrive at the conclusion that $\alpha(\lambda)$ varies by at most a few per cent in any 10-gm interval, included between, say, 100 and 300 gm. You might also conclude that $\alpha(\lambda)$ is nowhere enormously greater, say 1000 times greater, than even the smallest value that it attains between the bounds of 100 gm and 300 gm.

Armed with such knowledge, what could you conclude after weighing the potato on a tried and true balance known to have a normally distributed error with a standard deviation of 1 gm? Bayes's theorem, in this context, can be written

$$\alpha(\lambda \,|\, x) \;\propto\; \phi(x-\lambda)\,\alpha(\lambda), \tag{2}$$

where

$$\phi(z) = \frac{1}{\sqrt{(2\pi)}}\, e^{-\frac{1}{2}z^2}. \tag{3}$$

At first sight, (2) may seem inapplicable, because you know so little about $\alpha(\lambda)$. But suppose, for definiteness, that $x = 174\cdot3$ gm. As Fig. 1 shows, the function $\phi(174\cdot3 - \lambda)$ is almost zero outside the interval $174\cdot3 \pm 5$; the function $\alpha(\lambda)$ varies by at most a few per cent inside that interval and is never enormously larger outside the interval than it is inside of it. Under these circumstances, the product on the right side of (2) is well approximated for many purposes by

$$\phi(174\cdot3 - \lambda)\,\alpha(174\cdot3).$$

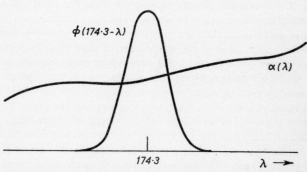

Fig. 1. Prior probability density $\alpha(\lambda)$ and likelihood $\phi\,(174\cdot3 - \lambda)$.

The probability density $\alpha(\lambda)$ and the likelihood $\phi(174\cdot3 - \lambda)$ are not drawn to the same vertical scale. Such quantities need not generally even be of the same dimension; with Poisson data, for instance, one would be probability per unit frequency, the other simply probability. Therefore, $\alpha(\lambda|x)$ is a probability density in λ that is well approximated by some constant multiple of $\phi(x - \lambda)$, but the only such multiple that is a probability density in λ, that is, the one that is suitably normalized, is clearly $\phi(x - \lambda)$ itself. Thus, after the weighing, your opinion about λ is expressed to a good degree of approximation by saying that λ is normally distributed around $174\cdot3$ gm with a standard deviation of 1. Though this is much the kind of conclusion that is usually ridiculed in the statistics classroom, I hope you now feel that, in the presence of reasonable assumptions about your own initial subjective probability, it is not ridiculous but true.

Note well that the example depends on two properties of $\alpha(\lambda)$, its near-constancy in the neighbourhood of the value of the observed value of x, and the relative moderateness of $\alpha(\lambda)$ far from that value. Both these properties of course refer to empirical facts about you and the potato. If, for example, you had weighed a potato yesterday that you thought might quite likely be the same potato that you are weighing today, $\alpha(\lambda)$ has a more or less sharp peak. If this initial peak lies close to x, then the assumption of near uniformity of $\alpha(\lambda)$ in the neighbourhood of x is violated; if the peak falls 4 or 5 gm away from x (and if you are all but certain that this is indeed the potato that you weighed yesterday), then the assumption of moderate behaviour of $\alpha(\lambda)$ distant from x fails to be satisfied.

The argument that led to $\phi(174\cdot3-\lambda)$ as your approximate final probability density for the weight of the potato is given and greatly generalized by Jeffreys (1948, section 3.4). But for the most part, especially in the reference just given, as opposed to Jeffreys (1957), Jeffreys would adopt a somewhat different line of thought, saying that, if you know nothing about the potato, $\alpha(\lambda)$ should be taken to be literally a constant. This is sometimes objected to on the grounds that such an $\alpha(\lambda)$ cannot be normalized; it is not literally a probability density. That objection does not seem terribly important to me because there do exist finitely additive probability measures corresponding to the idea of a uniform distribution on the whole line. To me, a more serious objection is that such a uniform distribution does not really represent the initial opinion of anybody, and surely does not represent an opinion that ought to be held by everybody, even apart from our sure knowledge that the weight of the potato is positive. This approach of Jeffreys, in effect, puts forward a valuable approximation as an exact conclusion. An interesting discussion of these ideas is given by Good (1950, p. 51).

Following, and in a few cases extending, Jeffreys (1948), many classical statistical situations can be treated in the spirit of the example about the potato. If a variance σ^2 is to be measured on the basis of a statistic s^2 with n degrees of freedom, your final distribution of σ^2 will (under favourable circumstances) be like that of ns^2/χ_n^2, where the data n and s^2 are of course regarded as fixed. This can be extended to the corresponding conclusion about a set of covariances in terms of

Wishart's distribution. If the parameters μ and σ^2 of a normal distribution are to be jointly estimated from $\bar{x}$, and s^2 based on n observations (and therefore $n-1$ degrees of freedom), then σ^2 is distributed as before with $n-1$ in place of n, and $n^{\frac{1}{2}}(\mu-\bar{x})/\sigma$ is, always speaking approximately, distributed independently of σ with a standard normal distribution; putting those facts together, the approximate final distribution of μ is like that of $\bar{x}+n^{-\frac{1}{2}}st_{n-1}$, where $\bar{x}$, n, s play the role of constants. This example generalizes to lead to a theory of regression and the analysis of variance formally similar to, but intellectually different from, the usual theory. Standard F distributions arise in connection with the distribution of the ratio of two unknown variances, beta distributions in connection with the estimation of a frequency from Bernoullian data, and gamma distributions in connection with the estimation of a Poisson parameter.

The Behrens-Fisher problem provides a particularly striking illustration of the theory, according to which the final distribution of two normal means when the means and variances are all grossly unknown is that of a certain linear combination of independent t-variables: this was shown in effect by Jeffreys (1948).

This is formally just the solution that has always been championed by Fisher. Fisher would say that it gives the exact fiducial probability, but I say only that it gives satisfactory approximate probabilities under suitable circumstances. The solution is not in even approximate agreement with confidence interval ideas; see Wallace (1959). In many cases, the theory of precise measurement tends to coincide in this way with the theory of fiducial probability, but the theory of precise measurement is not coterminal with the theory of fiducial probability (whatever the exact interpretation of the latter may be), because the theory of precise measurement is not dependent on the existence of sufficient statistics in the same sense as the theory of fiducial probability is and because the theory of precise measurement deals as well with discrete data as it does with continuous data.

The theory of precise measurement leads to a good understanding of the problem of estimating the ratio μ_1/μ_2 of two means from data of the form $\bar{x}_1$, $\bar{x}_2$, and s, or the closely related problem of estimating the direction of the vector (μ_1, μ_2). The approximate answer adduced here agrees with what I understand to be the one produced by the fiducial argument. This was given (for the problem of estimating the direction of the vector) by Creasy and confirmed by Fisher, who were in disagreement with Fieller; see Fieller *et al.* (1954).

The theory contributes to problems like the estimation of the difference of Poisson parameters or of variances, where convolutions of gamma distributions are invoked. However, these problems are often such that the difference is often known to be positive, which may well come into conflict with the hypotheses about gentle behaviour of the initial distribution necessary for the application of the theory of precise measurement. In such cases the problems must be considered anew and cannot be expected to have all of the advantages of precise measurements. Judging from experience with a problem that seems analogous to me, namely that of inferring an upper bound on a danger from a perfect safety record, even these less satisfactory situations can lead to useful inequalities. If a complete approximate final distribution does not occur in such problems, it is because the specification of the problem does not justify precise conclusions. Any theory – confidence intervals, fiducial probability, logical probabilities – that pretends to produce exactness where it is unjustified is a false servant.

5. Initial and final precision

With our great emphasis on operating characteristics, on how an experiment can be expected to perform, many of us have tended to forget the distinction between the precision that was to be expected from an experiment before it was performed and the precision actually yielded by it when it was performed. The confusion has been reinforced by the fact that for certain familiar kinds of experiments, the distinction really does vanish. The tendency to obliterate the distinction between initial and final precision is particularly natural to those objectivistic theories of statistics that officially refuse to discuss final or terminal opinions. Nonetheless, objectivists of both schools have pointed out the distinction in certain contexts.

A striking example concerning the estimation of the median of a uniform distribution of known range is sometimes discussed; see, for example, Lehmann (1959; p. 7, ex. 7) and the much earlier paper by Welch (1939).

We have been accustomed to think that if an estimator has a small mean square deviation, then an estimate resulting from the application of this estimator is in some sense trustworthy, but this is not true in general. An example of an estimator that is ordinarily trustworthy is the average of observations from a normal distribution with unit variance. These observations ordinarily constitute what was called in the last section a precise measurement of the unknown mean of the distribution, and there is then strong reason to suppose that the true mean μ lies close to the sample mean $\bar{x}$; and, in all cases, a sample from this normal family affects the final opinion only through $\bar{x}$.

On the other hand, the natural estimator for the median of a uniform distribution of unit range is the mid-range, that is, the average of the maximum and minimum observations. This estimator has a very small mean square deviation for large sample sizes, about $\frac{1}{2}n^{-2}$, and under usual initial opinions it can well claim to be the best possible estimator. But if, by accident, the range of the sample is very narrow, then the sample leaves grave doubts as to the position of the population median. In fact, the final distribution after such an observation is simply the initial distribution truncated to the interval from the maximum $-\frac{1}{2}$ to the minimum $+\frac{1}{2}$. If, for example, the maximum observation is $3\frac{1}{4}$ and the minimum $2\frac{1}{2}$, the median of the uniform distribution of unit range must be at least $3\frac{1}{4}-1+\frac{1}{2}=2\frac{3}{4}$ and at most $2\frac{1}{2}+1-\frac{1}{2}=3$; study of the likelihood shows that this is in fact all that the sample has to convey about the location of the median. If the initial distribution is sufficiently diffuse, then the final distribution is nearly uniform in the interval $2\frac{3}{4}$ to 3, no matter how large the sample was. The fact that the mean square deviation of the mid-range estimate is small corresponds to the fact that the final interval of nearly uniform uncertainty is almost always small, but this interval can occasionally be of almost unit length, in which case the sample is a relative failure.

Many other translation families exhibit much the same phenomenon. Consider the double exponential (or Laplace) distribution with density $\frac{1}{2}\exp(-|x-\mu|)$. The maximum likelihood estimate of the parameter μ is here the median of the sample. For large samples, its variance decreases nearly proportionally to $1/n$, and the Pitman (1939) estimate has a slightly smaller mean square deviation. Once more, this does not mean that an observation of a large sample for this distribution necessarily gives a sharp indication of the position of the median μ. If, for example, that there were two hundred observations of which one hundred fell beneath -1 and the other hundred above $+1$, the likelihood function would be a constant throughout the interval -1 to $+1$, and while the data may give strong evidence that the true value of μ is somewhere between the 100th and 101st observation, it gives no clue at all as to where in that interval μ is. The corresponding example (Fisher, 1934) for an odd sample size is not much less striking. The Cauchy distribution produces similar phenomena, and extensive observation of a Cauchy distribution can, very rarely to be sure, leave us with a sharply bimodal final distribution with the modes far separated from one another.

The examples just given are closely related to, and can be reformulated in terms of, a certain phenomenon about confidence intervals. For example, for the uniform distribution, the usual analogy between the theory of testing and confidence intervals suggests that the midrange of the sample $\pm \epsilon_n$ would be a good confidence interval for the median μ, with the constant ϵ_n suitably chosen. This is indeed a confidence interval, but it has distressing properties. If the range of the sample is in excess of $1 - 2\epsilon_n$, then we know with certainty that the interval contains the true value of μ, which was more than was bargained for. If the mid-range is unusually small, there is good evidence that the interval fails to cover μ. This evidence is meaningful even to objectivists of the Neyman-Pearson school, for it is easy to calculate that anyone who offers to pay 19 to 1 if the confidence interval misses the true value conditional on the mid-range's being unusually small stands to lose money. Even the system of confidence intervals based on what is technically called the best unbiased test of a null hypothesis about the mid-range has much the same unreasonable properties (Welch, 1939).

There is some literature, mostly objectivistic, devoted to this phenomenon of confidence intervals that are, so to speak, not conditional confidence intervals. One reference, leading to others, is Wallace (1959). So far as problems of translation are concerned, confidence intervals proposed by Pitman (1939) meet the situation, and, in fact, agree with intervals that would be generated from the theory of precise measurement by taking intervals from the centre of the approximate final distribution with specified probability.

A prominent instance in which the outlook of the Neyman-Pearson school led to neglect of the difference between precision promised and precision delivered is the Stein two-sample procedure (Stein, 1945) for producing a confidence interval of fixed length, say one, for normal distributions of unknown mean and unknown variance, as has been mentioned by Lindley (1958). The general idea here is to use a pilot sample with mean $\bar{x}'$ and sample standard deviation s' and then to adopt a total sample size N that promises to be large enough to ensure the required precision. If $\bar{x}$ is the mean of the whole sample, then (except for slight approximations) $\bar{x} \pm \frac{1}{2}$ is a confidence interval at the required confidence level and the problem is formally solved. Stein actually proposed certain refinements to take account of the discreteness of the integers and of the possibility that the first sample is already more than adequate. These refinements need not detain us here, but in common sense they are steps in the wrong practical direction, as Stein points out, for they waste data to avoid justifying a conclusion of more precision than is required. Now, if the Stein procedure is carried out, and if it happens, as it occasionally will, that the standard deviation s of the whole sample is much larger than s', then there is good evidence that the interval $\bar{x} \pm \frac{1}{2}$ has missed its mark. Once more, the evidence can be called objective. The ingenious procedure that was widely acclaimed in the statistical climate of 1945 has since been seen by frequentists, including its author, and by personalists to have the serious defect just pointed out.

Incidentally, the concept of precise measurement immediately suggests a good practical solution to the kind of practical situation that gave rise to Stein's problem. If you want to weigh a potato on a balance of highly unknown standard deviation sufficiently frequently to be able justifiably to give odds of 99 to 1 that the true weight μ of the potato lies in an interval 0·1 gm long, the natural and I believe the right thing to do is this. Simply weigh the potato repeatedly until you find that the middle 99 per cent of your final (or better, intermediate) distribution has a length of 0·1 gm. This is practical, because after the first four or five weighings, your intermediate distribution will typically be well approximated with the aid of the t-distribution of

$n-1$ degrees of freedom. An interesting objectivistic discussion of this and related methods is given by Anscombe (1954).

6. Sharp null hypotheses

To give you an illustration of the application of subjective probability outside of precise measurement, I shall say something about testing sharp null hypotheses, mainly in the form of an allegory, though I still know too little about this application of subjective probability.

At least three different situations are commonly crowded into a common Procrustean bed in the name of testing a null hypothesis. There are still other situations that used to be confused with these but that are less often now (Bahadur and Robbins, 1950). These three situations have been poorly distinguished, when distinguished at all, because the real differences among them are largely differences in initial probabilities, about which objectivists have no adequate vocabulary. Let me illustrate by telling three versions of the legend of King Hiero's crown.

In all three versions the king knows or suspects that his goldsmiths have adulterated the gold of his new crown. Archimedes, under delightful circumstances, hits on the idea of determining the density of the crown by weighing it and a specimen of pure gold in air and water. It does no important violence to the story to suppose that Archimedes has in effect measured a number λ, with the error of measurement normally distributed with standard deviation σ about λ. The crown is either unadulterated, denser than pure gold, or less dense than pure gold according as $\lambda = 0, \lambda > 0$, or $\lambda < 0$. I choose to forget here that the presumed adulterant was silver, which would lighten the crown; retaining that feature would lead to one-sided tests.

It is odd, though not unthinkable, that Archimedes and the king should know σ, but this helps keep the example down to essentials. Archimedes may in fact have made and averaged many measurements. Why he made just the number he did is another story, but once he stops, the average is in effect a single measurement as postulated.

Depending on his source of information and on his objectives, Hiero might be imagined to have one of the following sorts of initial attitudes, among others.

Version 1. The king is sure that there has been cheating, and his opinion about its extent is diffuse with respect to Archimedes's measurement. The king would like to decide whether the crown is denser, or less dense, than gold. But he is willing and free to abstain from deciding if the evidence is inconclusive.

Version 2. The king is sure that there has been cheating, but his opinion is not diffuse. Rather, he feels with considerable confidence that $|\lambda| < 2\sigma$. Once more he would like, if possible, to decide whether the crown is denser or less dense than gold. This version is the most difficult and the one of most prominence in realistic statistical practice and thinking.

Version 3. The king attaches some credence, be it large or small, to the possibility that there has been no cheating ($\lambda = 0$), and his opinion about the extent of the cheating, conditional on there being some, is diffuse with respect to the measurement. He wants to hang the goldsmiths if they are at all guilty, otherwise not.

According to many objectivistic textbooks, the king's response to a measurement x should be about the same in all three versions. He should, it is implied, select some small probability α, say $\alpha = 0.05$, 0.01, or 0.001, at his discretion. He should then compute the probability that $t = x/\sigma$ would be at least as large as the observed value if λ were 0, that is

$$1 - \int_{-|t|}^{+|t|} \phi(z)\,dz = \Phi(-|t|) + \{1 - \Phi(|t|)\}$$
$$= 2\Phi(-|t|).$$

If this value is less than his α, he should reject the null hypothesis, otherwise accept it. For Versions 1 and 2, rejection means to take the sign of x seriously as an indication of the sign of λ. For Version 3, it means to hang the goldsmiths.

An alternative textbook doctrine that might be offered is not to reject at any fixed α but to regard $\alpha(t) = 2 - 2\Phi(|t|)$ as some kind of measure of the doubt the king should have were he to reject the null hypothesis. You shall see that both objectivistic doctrines are inappropriate to Version 1 and especially inappropriate to Versions 2 and 3. No version for which they are appropriate is known to me.

In Version 1, the king feels rather sure before making the measurement that he will obtain practically unequivocal information about the sign of λ, which is what he wants to know in this version. He might, for example, be willing to bet 100 to 1 that $|x|$ will be found to exceed 4σ. If $|x|$ is in fact that large, the principles of precise measurement will leave the king little doubt about the sign of λ, though (under typical circumstances) it would be an abuse of those principles to attempt thus to measure this small doubt by other than a rough upper bound. If, however, x does happen to fall within, say, 3σ or 4σ of 0, the king may, under favourable circumstances, find that $\Phi(-|t|)$ is about the probability for him that the sign of λ is not that of x. Note that $\Phi(-|t|)$ is not $\alpha(t)$ but $\frac{1}{2}\alpha(t)$, so that neither textbook doctrine is quite appropriate to Version 1.

In Version 2, the king rather expects to find x within 2σ of zero. If this does in fact happen, his terminal distribution of λ, and in particular his terminal probability that λ is positive, depends quite sensitively on the behaviour of his initial distribution of λ near $\lambda = 0$. This distribution was not adequately specified in the description of the problem, and, in particular, it may be very asymmetrical. Still more, the king may not know his own mind well enough to specify adequately the behaviour of his initial distribution of λ. In this case, the experiment will inescapably leave him in a quandary. Any theory that pretends to do more, to reach a conclusion about the sign of λ without using the king's initial opinion, goes too far. What can be hoped for is useful inequalities.

Version 3 has an interesting theory for which we are indebted to Jeffreys (1948), who presents both special cases and general theory. Lindley also discovered a broad generalization of this theory some years ago, which will be published shortly (Lindley, 1961).

Let I be the king's initial probability that $\lambda = 0$. Let $\pi(\lambda)$ be his (diffuse) initial density for λ given that $\lambda \neq 0$. The corresponding final quantities I' and $\pi'(\lambda)$ are determined through Bayes's theorem by

$$I' = \frac{C}{\sigma} \phi(x/\sigma) I = \frac{C}{\sigma} \phi(t) I \tag{1}$$

and

$$I' \pi'(\lambda) = \frac{C}{\sigma} \phi\left(\frac{x-\lambda}{\sigma}\right) I\pi(\lambda). \tag{2}$$

Integrate (2), recalling that π is supposed to be diffuse relative to ϕ, to conclude that

$$\bar{I}' \simeq C\pi(x)\bar{I}, \tag{3}$$

provided t is not enormous; otherwise, there is strong but ill-measured evidence of guilt.

The division of (1) by (3) yields an approximation for the final odds in favour of innocence ($\lambda = 0$),

$$\frac{I'}{\bar{I}'} \simeq \frac{\phi(t)}{\sigma} \cdot \frac{1}{\pi(x)} \cdot \frac{I}{\bar{I}}. \tag{4}$$

It is gratifying to find that the terminal odds are a multiple of the initial odds. The one other aspect of the king's initial opinion about λ that enters is $\pi(x)$. Objectivistic doctrine would suggest that the only thing important about the measurement for the king's decision should be the 'double tail-area' $\alpha(t)$. Actually, it is not through $\alpha(t)$ but through the density $\phi(t)$ that t enters, and σ plays a role as well as t.

Precedence for the importance of σ here can probably be found in the writings of objectivists, but, broadly speaking, it is in contrast with objectivistic theorizing.

The king will hang the goldsmiths if $I'/\bar{I}'$ is large enough. He may be hard pressed to tell himself how large is large enough or to evaluate the personal factor $I/(\pi(x)\bar{I})$. This lack of self-knowledge may leave him in a quandary, but often t and σ will be such that very rough values of the personal factor and the critical odds suffice. Also, in real life, the king might be able to make a new measurement if in doubt or to accept the risk of excusing slight guilt as relatively unimportant or to do still other things that would ameliorate his dilemma.

The general theory developed by Jeffreys and Lindley for problems like Version 3 is adequate to deal with nuisance parameters. Various double dichotomy problems now normally treated by χ^2 with one degree of freedom are a good testing ground for this theory; some exploration is carried out by Jeffreys (1948, sections 5.11–5.14; 1957, section 3.6).

One thing that I have tried to convey in this section is what seems to become of the theory of testing hypotheses when it is studied through subjective probability, but this is not a topic that I could cover fully here, even if there were space. In particular, it would be challenging to offer a clear analysis of 'shotgun tests'. Friends have emphasized that real life seems to offer few problems at all like Version 3; I agree and conclude, with those friends, that hypothesis testing is not nearly of such widespread appropriateness as many who routinely use statistics seem to think.

7. Conclusion

Every topic in statistics ought to be reviewed in the light of the concept of subjective probability, but certain broad problems seem particularly important at present.

First, there are many situations like precise measurement, except that an infinite (or at least unlimited) number of parameters are involved, and typically we do not expect to have enough information to measure all of them precisely but only to measure precisely a few functions of the infinite set of parameters. The problem of five-year survival mentioned in section 3 is a case in point. Another, and a typical problem of non-parametric statistics, is to measure the median or other percentage points of a largely unknown distribution function. Whittle (1957, 1958) has recently applied subjective probability to curve-fitting and to the estimation of the autocorrelation function of a stochastic process. Both these problems are further illustrations of what I meant to suggest by an unlimited number of unknown parameters, and it would be good to see the impetus given by Whittle followed up.

Many feel intuitively that there are circumstances that do call for application of the traditional tests, like F tests and χ^2 tests. Where, if anywhere, this intuition is justified, I am confident that it will not be found at variance with the concept of subjective probability, but the situation has not yet been properly analysed and explored.

Again, though we all feel sure that randomization is an important invention, the theory of subjective probability reminds us that we have not fully understood randomization. It is not enough to say something like this: 'If you randomize here, you are very unlikely to make a mistake.' It can happen that when the randomization is done, the

C

experimenter sees that he has made a mistake, that is, sees that the experiment called for by the randomization is inappropriate. This point has been studied by several who probably think of themselves as objectivists (Grundy and Healy, 1950; Jones, 1958; Yates, 1951a, b). In particular, randomization could accidentally closely correlate any variable that has not been controlled by stratification or some such device, with one of the treatments. For example, we might accidentally choose at random a latin square with the treatments running in regular slanting lines across the field. It would usually be most ill-advised to carry out such an experiment in which treatment is highly correlated with a possible gradient in fertility merely because this bad design had arisen at random.

The problem of analysing the idea of randomization is more acute, and at present more baffling, for subjectivists than for objectivists, more baffling because an ideal subjectivist would not need randomization at all. He would simply choose the specific layout that promised to tell him the most. The need for randomization presumably lies in the imperfection of actual people and, perhaps, in the fact that more than one person is ordinarily concerned with an investigation. The imperfections of real people with respect to subjective probability are vagueness and temptation to self-deception, as has been explained, and randomization properly employed may perhaps alleviate both of these defects.

Other problems that seem to concern self-discipline are those of dealing with outlying observations and with empirical surprises generally. Here again, subjective probability gives a simple solution in principle. For example, an observation ought to be regarded as due to a gross error if and only if Bayes's theorem tells us that it probably is, but vagueness and temptation make it particularly difficult to apply this simple maxim. Again, self-discipline is often enforced by using part of the data to suggest ideas and the rest of it to confirm these ideas. This process is not really easy to understand and appraise. In particular, there seems to be little cogent advice as to what fraction of the data should be used for exploration and what fraction for confirmation. Half and half is often suggested, but without particularly good reason. One interesting discussion of this problem of hindsight is by Simon (1953).

In this lecture, I have emphasized applications of subjective probability that do not depend sensitively on many details of the initial probabilities. Such robustness is important when it occurs, but we must remember that statistics presents many problems that are not robust in this sense. The problem of choosing a sample size (and some other design parameters) is an especially conspicuous example. Even in these cases, it is, I believe, far better to use the concept of subjective probability to order our thoughts than to try to make the necessary choices by unformalized intuition.

I hope that even though you may not yet fully share my enthusiasm, you have come to feel that subjective probability promises to make important contributions to statistical theory. The improvements are so simple and far-reaching that they are by no means confined to academic theorizing but should have an immediate impact on our teaching and consulting.

PART II

Prepared Contributions

PROFESSOR M. S. BARTLETT

I understood that this conference was to be informal in character, and I have not prepared any detailed statement of my own views, which have been expounded before on various occasions; see, for example, some of the papers in my Essays (Bartlett, 1962).

What one hopes for in a conference of this kind is an understanding of differing viewpoints, and if possible some reconciliation of them. Let me suggest therefore that divergent opinions be honestly recognized by all the interested parties as, in inference at least, no one method can be claimed to be the only method that people do or should use. I have listed various definitions of statistics and statistical inference either directly or indirectly implied in the rather miscellaneous collection of quotations given below, which I frankly admit are highly selected and biased, and make no claim to comprehensiveness. They do, however, support my claim that we have to recognize many antagonistic points of view, which I will try to summarize as follows (the *a* and *b* versions of each pair of statements being in some sense or other rival versions):

1a Statistics are facts or observations, not necessarily about the State.

1b Historically, both in science and in popular language, statistics are about aggregates or populations of individuals or events, and their properties as a group or on the average.

2a Statistical inference is inductive inference.

2b Statistical inference is inference from statistics.

3a Many people, but not all, advocate a statistical or frequency theory of probability.

3b Many people, but not all, advocate the explicit use of other, e.g. prior, probabilities and possibly utilities.

(i) Some of these regard these probabilities as personal and subjective.

(ii) Some claim they are impersonal and objective.

Having noted these various approaches, I should perhaps indicate briefly my own position. I would myself emphasize the historical association of statistics with populations and aggregates, and note that statisticians who recognize this character of statistics will necessarily recognize the frequency theory of probability. This bifurcation of probability theory, which has been recognized by many writers, including philosophers, such as Carnap (1950), naturally affects the way in which statistical inferences are made, because statisticians, such as myself, who favour the frequency theory prefer to base their arguments as far as possible on such generally accepted probabilities and not on the so-called subjective or 'degree of belief' types of probability. The fact that we avoid as far as possible explicit use of such probabilities does not imply that our inferences are any the less rational; we simply prefer to keep the two types of probability separate.

Quotations

'This science (the theory of probability) has for its main task the study of group phenomena, that is, such phenomena as occur in collections of a large number of objects of essentially the same kind.' (Khinchin, 1949, p. 1.)

'It dawns upon us that the individual case is entirely devoid of interest, whether detailed information about it is obtainable or not, whether the mathematical problem it sets can be coped with or not. We realize that even if it could be done, we should have to follow up thousands of individual cases and could eventually make no better use of them than compound them into one statistical enunciation. The working of the statistical mechanism itself is what we are really interested in.' (Schrödinger, 1944.)

'The science of statistics is essentially a branch of Applied Mathematics, and may be regarded as mathematics applied to observational data.' (Fisher, 1925, p. 1.)

'In terms of Fisher's definition I would describe statistical theory as a mathematical theory which relates to observational data arising from a physical background of chance.' (Bartlett, 1940.)

'By statistical data and statistical phenomena I refer to numerical and quantitative facts about groups or classes of individuals or events, rather than facts about the individuals themselves. . . .

Now we can try to see what is meant by statistical inference. It is inference from statistical data, and makes use of its own intrinsic theoretical concepts associated with the regularity properties of statistical groups or populations, and formulated mathematically in terms of the theory of probability.' (Bartlett, 1962; taken from unpublished lecture of 1956.)

'In this name [mathematical statistics], "mathematical" seems to be intended to connote rational, theoretical, or perhaps mathematically advanced, to distinguish the subject from those problems of gathering and condensing numerical data that can be considered apart from the problem of inductive inference, the mathematical treatment of which is generally relatively trivial. The name "statistical inference" recognizes that the subject is concerned with inductive inference.' (Savage, 1954, p. 2.)

'In recent years, Statistics has been formulated as the science of decision making under uncertainty.' (Chernoff and Moses, 1959, preface.)

'I shall call them "Bayes" probabilities because, frequency or not, they are the ones needed for insertion into Bayes's theorem. Savage argues that they are "personalistic", that is, they are a property of the individual and not of society. I would dispute this myself, and agree with Jeffreys in saying that in scientific questions they are objective. They only differ between individuals because the individuals are differently informed; but with common knowledge we have common Bayesian probabilities. We can ignore this side-issue in the present account.' (Lindley, 1958.)

'Subjective expectations, valuations and preferences and their changes from person [to person] or in the course of time can and should be investigated by means of "objective" statistical methods. Trying to use them as a basis of statistics is like trying to gauge a fever thermometer by means of the patient's shivers.' (van Dantzig, 1957.)

PROFESSOR G. A. BARNARD

Statistical inference is that part of scientific inference in which quantitative measures of uncertainty are employed. If we leave on one side the purely philosophic doubt that should perhaps be in our minds at all times, then not all scientific inference is uncertain, and not all uncertainty is quantifiable with concepts now available. So statistical inference is a proper part of scientific inference, not the whole of it; though with the evolution of new concepts to measure new kinds of uncertainty, the domain of statistical inference may grow without limit. If, as the results of Löwenheim and Godel teach us, no formal limit can be set to valid modes of purely mathematical reasoning, so *a fortiori* one would expect no formal limit to valid modes of the wider field of statistical reasoning.

Some like to use the word probability to cover all quantitative measures of uncertainty, distinguishing the different kinds by adjectives such as 'subjective', 'physical', 'rational', 'pistimetric', and so forth. Others, including myself, feel that the differences are so important, and require such emphasis at the present time, as to be best dealt with by the use of different nouns, such as 'likelihood', 'acceptability', and 'long-run frequency', as well as probability itself. But we surely should not devote much time to a purely verbal dispute about whether adjectives or nouns should be used. We do, unfortunately, have to devote some time to describing the particular usage we adopt.

For my part I follow Fisher (see, for example, his papers in the pamphlet *Smoking and Lung Cancer* (Fisher, 1958), which, for half-a-crown, is a very good bargain for someone who wants to read a profound discussion of the nature of probability) in preferring to restrict the term probability to that kind of precisely measurable uncertainty the concept of which arose in connection with games of chance in the seventeenth century, when it became possible to manufacture reasonably 'fair' dice and reasonably uniform packs of cards. In relation to a single throw of a fair die, the concept of a hypothetical infinite population of throws, to which the particular one considered belongs, and one-sixth of which result (for example) in a three, is natural; and the impossibility of a gambling system, or martingale, corresponds to our inability to specify a subset of the infinite population, to which a throw under consideration belongs, and with which any fraction other than one-sixth can be attached. To say that any proposition has a probability of one-sixth, therefore, for me means that my knowledge of the proposition differs only in subject matter, not in quality or quantity, from my knowledge of the proposition that the die will turn up 'three'. It implies uncertainty, but uncertainty of a specially precise kind. On the other hand there are many propositions on which, if I were a betting man, I would be prepared to bet five to one against, concerning which my knowledge is much less precise than my knowledge of the die; such propositions would not, for me, have a probability, though they would have a plausibility which was measurable in a loose way by reference to the betting odds. The word 'probability', as I prefer to use it, refers to the most precisely measurable kind of uncertainty; other forms of uncertainty are, I think, best referred to by other words, like 'plausibility', 'acceptability', and so forth.

Before continuing with the discussion of statistical inference it is necessary to refer to a topic which, in my opinion, is distinct from inference, namely, decision-making. That there is a distinction seems to me to follow from the fact that in decision-making it is necessary to specify a goal to be aimed at in the result of the decision, whereas inferences can be made without reference to any such goal. To equate decision-making with inference is tantamount to pragmatism; as with other theories of truth, pragmatism is not wholly false, and it serves to emphasize important aspects, but it cannot be accepted as wholly adequate. It is certainly true that many statistical decision problems are still wrongly treated as if they were problems of statistical inference; the pendulum may have swung too far towards decision-making in the upper reaches of abstract statistical theory, but in the more concrete sphere of applications it has not yet swung far enough. This overforwardness of theory, combined with lag in application, is due, in my opinion, to the attempt to embrace statistical inference within statistical decision theory. This attempt has led to a misguided search for general principles, such as the minimax principle (Wald, 1950) or the unbiasedness principle (Lehmann, 1959), which attempt to get rid of the essential indeterminacy of the decision problem as usually formulated. A frank recognition of the (limited) degree of indeterminacy that attaches to nearly all practical decision problems would greatly facilitate their solution. I am most certainly with Professor Savage in his call for more use of Bayesian methods in practical statistics.

In applying probability theory to decision-making we consider the expected gain or loss. This seems to me to imply that we are concerned with what happens in a 'long run' of similar decision situations. We may suppose that in such a 'long run' the various 'states of nature' (hypotheses) will occur with definite 'long-run frequencies' which define a 'prior distribution'. This prior distribution is not (usually) a distribution of probability, but rather a distribution of long-run frequency. However, it can be proved that we get the best decision rule, in a given long run, by applying Bayes's theorem to the prior distribution defined by the long run, if this prior distribution is known. If it is unknown, then the problem of getting the best decision rule is indeterminate, like the problem: $10x + y = 21$, what is x? Here the unknown y corresponds to the unknown prior distribution, while x corresponds to the best decision rule. Sometimes we may guess that y is small, and so deduce that x is about 2; similarly, we may guess that a prior distribution is reasonably smooth, so that the likelihood function itself will give a fair approximation to the posterior distribution. But if we really have no idea of what the prior distribution is like, then we can have no rational idea of what to do, and we can only make guesses. However, people's wills do not enter into these guesses, so that these guessed prior distributions should not be described as personal. Whoever manages to guess the prior distribution most accurately will obtain the best decision rule.

Decision situations, where Bayesian principles of this kind are applicable, occur frequently in industrial applications of statistics. In such cases we are commonly concerned with routine decisions, and some empirical evidence concerning long-run frequencies is often available, as, for example, with sampling inspection, where the prior distribution, or process curve as it is called in this instance, can in principle be estimated from past records. The subjective approach to probability is at a disadvantage here, because it puts the emphasis in the wrong place, suggesting that we should perform acts of intro-spection in order to establish the prior distribution, rather than collect records. This wrong emphasis of the subjective theory leads to neglect of some important aspects of Bayesian decision theory. For example, from a subjective point of view it is hard to think of a lumped prior distribution as being appropriate for a continuously variable parameter. Yet lumped distributions have properties which make them often the most convenient type of parameter distributions to use. Again, in relation to a given experiment it has often proved useful to specify the prior distribution by reference to the 'non-contradiction principle'. This is an application of the elementary logic of the simple test of significance to the more sophisticated problems of choice between statistical hypotheses such as are involved in statistical decisions. It consists in noting that the prior distribution must be such that for any conceivable experimental result there must be an hypothesis H having positive prior probability which is not significantly rejected by the result E. The non-contradiction principle, with the use of lumped distributions, and perhaps variance considerations, when appropriate, often serve to specify prior distributions with all the precision needed for practical applications.

To return to statistical inference, it is necessary to classify problems somewhat differently from the way which has become usual in textbooks of mathematical statistics. Instead of the usual division into 'testing hypotheses', 'estimation', with its subdivision into 'interval' and 'point estimation', and 'discrimination' we prefer to consider

(a) the comparison of data E with a single statistical hypothesis, H, leading to simple tests of significance;

(b) simple preference problems, in which, on the basis of data E, we rank a family of simple hypotheses $H(\theta)$ in order of credibility;

(c) composite preference problems, in which, on the basis of data E, we wish to rank a family of composite hypotheses.

This enumeration of types of problem is not, of course, exhaustive, and it is not intended to exclude the consideration of the same body of data from several different points of view.

As to (a), we require first of all a criterion serving to rank E amongst other possible experimental results, in order of discrepancy from what is to be expected if H is true. The measure of discrepancy chosen will depend on the way in which H is interpreted, and on other matters involving scientific judgement. We must, of course, have in mind some scientifically meaningful alternative possibility to H, and our choice of measure of discrepancy will reflect our alternative conceptions to this extent. But we need not have in mind any statistically specified alternative hypotheses, as Neyman would suggest; indeed, if the alternatives are fully specified as statistical hypotheses, we shall have a preference problem rather than a simple testing problem.

The earliest serious test of significance on record seems to be that from which Daniel Bernoulli inferred that the (oriented) planes of the planetary orbits (as represented by their poles on the celestial sphere) were too close together to be reasonably consistent with the hypothesis that they were randomly and independently distributed. This example serves to illustrate well the fact that no statistically specified alternative needs to be considered to make a test of significance valid. The idea that the planetary orbits might tend to be coplanar, or nearly so, was clearly meaningful in the context of Newtonian mechanics and the theory of gravitation current at the time, but theories of the origin of the solar system were not then developed (they are hardly so even now) to the point where statistically definite alternatives to the null hypothesis could be considered.

Bernoulli's test illustrates another point in connection with tests of significance, namely that the measure of discrepancy used may be to some extent arbitrary. He first considered as a measure the size of the smallest circle which would include all the representative points on the surface of the sphere; the probability of a circle as small or smaller than that observed was so remote as to represent what Bernoulli called a 'moral impossibility'. He also considered the mean distance of the points representing the other planets from that representing the earth, and found that this also corresponded to a remotely improbable value. The fact that both measures of discrepancy led to low probabilities enable the null hypothesis to be firmly rejected. Had the two measures given conflicting answers, the issue would have remained in doubt, though this doubt might have been resolved by further, more precise, considerations.

Other points of complication arising with tests of significance may be illustrated by reference to the 2×2 table:

	A	not-A	Total
Sample I	a	c	m
Sample II	b	d	n
	r	s	N

If the probability of A is p_1 in the population from which I is a random sample, and p_2 in that from which II is a random sample, we wish to test the hypothesis $H(p)$ that $p_1 = p_2 = p$. At first sight it may seem that a suitable measure of 'discrepancy' would be the apparent difference in relative frequency, namely

$$\frac{a}{m} - \frac{b}{n},$$

but the variability of this changes with p in such a way as to leave us in doubt whether the difference

$$\frac{10}{100} - \frac{5}{100} = 0.05$$

does or does not represent as big a discrepancy as the difference

$$\frac{50}{100} - \frac{45}{100} = 0.05.$$

We are led to see that the discrepancy ranking can be made unambiguous in several ways: by restricting consideration to the set S_1 of tables having the same column totals (r, s) as the given one, or to the set S_2 of tables having the same values of (a, c) as the given one, or the set S_3 of those having the same values (b, d). The set S_1 is the only one of these, however, on which the conditional distribution defined by the null hypothesis is free from the nuisance parameter p, and so it is this S_1 which is chosen as the reference set.

We obtain an example of a preference problem, case (b), if we consider the 2×2 table as far as it throws light on the relative credibility of different pairs of values of (p_1, p_2). From this point of view the whole of the relevant information is contained in the likelihood function

$$L(p_1,p_2) = \frac{p_1^a(1-p_1)^c \, p_2^b(1-p_2)^d}{\left(\dfrac{a}{m}\right)^a \left(\dfrac{c}{m}\right)^c \left(\dfrac{b}{n}\right)^b \left(\dfrac{d}{n}\right)^d},$$

which is here, as usual, normalized by making

$$\sup_{p_1,\, p_2} L = 1.$$

By drawing the contours

$$L(p_1, p_2) = \text{const}$$

in the unit square representing all possible values of (p_1,p_2), we can see how the given data rank these values, in order of likelihood.

Likelihood is a measure of credibility of a precise kind, which has a weaker mathematical structure than has probability, in that the probabilities of two mutually exclusive events, E, F, determine (by the addition rule) the probability of their disjunction, E or F, but the likelihoods of two mutually exclusive hypotheses, H_1, H_2, do not, by themselves, serve to determine that of their disjunction, H_1 or H_2.

If we need an interpretation of likelihood, it can be obtained in two principal ways. Directly, if we find, for example, that

$$L(0{\cdot}1, 0{\cdot}1) = 0{\cdot}9,$$

while

$$L(0{\cdot}2, 0{\cdot}05) = 0{\cdot}01,$$

we can say that as between the two hypotheses represented by these two pairs of values of (p_1,p_2), the odds are 90 to 1 in favour of the first. This implies that further evidence providing a likelihood ratio at least as large as this, in the opposite sense, would be needed before, on the combined data, the first hypothesis was no more strongly supported than the second. For example, if an event E were just $1{\cdot}57$ times as probable on the second hypothesis as on the first, since $(1{\cdot}57)^{10} = 90$, we would require evidence equivalent to ten occurrences of such an event before considering the combined data as favouring neither hypothesis.

Alternatively we can interpret a likelihood ratio by reference to a hypothetical set of repetitions of experiments, in which we imagine Wald's 'sequential probability ratio' procedure to be used. We interpret the likelihood ratio of 90:1 for H versus H' by considering a long run of sequential 'tests' of one simple hypothesis against another, in every one of which the likelihood ratio of 90:1, or 1:90, is achieved before stopping. Such a test procedure will be associated with a 'risk of error of the first kind' (or of the second kind) of $1/91$, or, odds of error 90:1 against. These odds will be interpreted in a direct probability sense, as those associated with such a test procedure when one or other of the competing hypotheses is given as true.

Neither of these interpretations of likelihood relies in any way on the idea of a prior probability for the hypotheses considered. If we feel, in a given case, able to make use of such an idea, then the likelihood ratio is very simply interpreted, as the factor by which the prior probability ratio is multiplied to give the posterior probability ratio. In particular, in the important case when all hypotheses have the same prior probability, the likelihood function and the posterior probability function differ, if at all, only by a normalizing constant.

The problem of testing hypotheses, as formulated by Neyman and Pearson, belongs in my opinion to the present category of preference problems. According to Neyman and Pearson, we are given a sample space S, with typical point x and measure μ, and a parameter space Ω, with typical point θ, and a function $\phi(x|\theta)$ defined on the product $S \times \Omega$ which, for each fixed θ, is a probability function in S. The parameter space Ω is divided into two sets, ω and its complement $\Omega - \omega$, corresponding to the 'hypothesis tested', H_0 and the 'alternative hypothesis', H_1; the 'testing problem' then consist in dividing S into a set C, the critical region, and its complement $S - C$, such that if the observed point x falls in C we 'reject H_0 in favour of H_1', whereas if x falls in $S - C$ we 'accept H_0', or at least 'fail to reject H_0'. The power function associated with the critical region C is the probability that x will be in C, as a function of θ,

$$P(\theta|C) = \int\limits_{C} \phi(x|\theta)\, d\mu.$$

For any fixed choice of C we can imagine that the experiment consists, not in finding which x in S is to be observed, but merely whether the event 'x in C', or its negation 'x in $S - C$' is observed. If we denote the first of these events by E, it is then apparent that the likelihood function of θ, given E,

$$L(\theta|E) = \frac{\int\limits_C \phi(x|\theta)\,d\mu}{\sup\limits_\theta \int\limits_C \phi(x|\theta)\,d\mu}$$

is, apart possibly from a normalization constant, the same as the power function $P(\theta|C)$. Thus the power function is the likelihood function, given that a significant α result has been obtained.

It would be out of place here to develop in detail the relationship between $P(\theta|C)$ and $L(\theta|E)$ and $L(\theta|x)$. However, it should be noted that whenever two distinct points on the power curve are compared, as for example in Neyman's definition of an unbiased test:

$$P(\theta|C) \geqslant P(\theta_0|C) \quad \text{for all } \theta \neq \theta_0,$$

there is an implicit use of the notion of likelihood; the comparison of probabilities calculated on distinct, mutually exclusive hypotheses can have no meaning of a purely probabilistic kind.

From the present point of view, if it is accepted that the object in a 'testing problem' as posed by Neyman and Pearson, is to compare the 'plausibilities' of $H_0: \theta$ in ω and $H_1: \theta$ in $\Omega - \omega$, it would seem reasonable to do so by comparing the mean level of the likelihood $L(\theta|x)$ in ω and in $\Omega - \omega$, i.e. to consider the 'average likelihood ratio'

$$R(x) = \frac{\int\limits_\omega L(\theta|x)\,d\theta}{\int\limits_{\Omega-\omega} L(\theta|x)\,d\theta},$$

where $d\theta$ denotes some suitably chosen integrating measure. The $R(x)$ thus introduced is near to Wilks's ratio

$$W(x) = \frac{\sup\limits_\omega L(\theta|x)}{\sup\limits_{\Omega-\omega} L(\theta|x)}$$

and $R(x)$ may be used as a test criterion, as $W(x)$ is commonly so used. The function $R(x)$ has the advantage over $W(x)$ of not giving rise to inadmissible test procedures.

Before leaving preference problems I would like to re-emphasize a plea I have made before, for a study of the types of likelihood function which can arise in practical statistical problems. It happens in very many cases indeed that $\log L(\theta)$ is very well approximated by a quadratic function of the coordinates θ_i of θ; and in such cases a good description of the likelihood function is obtained by quoting the maximum likelihood estimator of θ, $\hat{\theta}$, together with the second derivatives $\partial^2/\partial\theta_i^2$, $\partial^2/\partial\theta_i\,\partial\theta_j$ of $\log L(\theta)$ at $\hat{\theta}$. It is a pity that the asymptotic equivalence of these derivatives, under regularity conditions, to elements of the invariance matrix of the estimates $\hat{\theta}_i$ has obscured the more important non-asymptotic interpretation in terms of a paraboloidal log-likelihood function.

It can happen that the parabolic approximation to $\log L(\theta)$ is poor and in such cases other approximations may be useful. Fisher has already noted the possibility of considering the series of higher order derivatives of $\log L(\theta)$, from which $\log L(\theta)$ can be constructed by means of the Taylor series, and we may content ourselves here with noting that in other cases it may be more appropriate to use the series of moments, which in the one-dimensional case are

$$\mu_r = \int_\Omega \theta^r L(\theta)\,d\theta \qquad (r = 0, 1, 2, \ldots)$$

instead of the Taylor coefficients. The moment series could be combined with any system of curves fitted by moments (for example, the Gram-Charlier series) to give an approximation to the true $L(\theta)$ from the series of μ_r. However, all such methods of approximating to likelihood functions will become less important when large automatic computers enable us to trace the whole course of the likelihood function without difficulty.

Coming finally to problems of the third category, an example of this is provided by that of fitting a polynomial to a set of observed values of a variable y, corresponding to various values of an independent variable x. All sorts of empirical rules have been given for deciding when to stop including terms in x of higher degree, but none of these rules seems able to withstand logical scrutiny, unless we introduce some idea such as one we have ventured to call 'accept-ability'. According to this, the reason why we fit, for example, a cubic term after fitting terms up to the second degree,

$$y = a_0 + a_1 x + a_2 x^2 (+ a_3 x^3) + \text{error},$$

instead of jumping, say, to the seventh degree,

$$y = a_0 + a_1 x + a_2 x^2 (+ a_7 x^7) + \text{error},$$

is, that in some sense x^3 is 'more acceptable' than x^7. The notion of acceptability involved here can be quantified, in the context of a family of functions such as the polynomials here considered, which exhibit lattice structure, and certain other special features. It serves to make explicit many of our preconceptions concerning the nature of our experimental material, and the sorts of law which it may be expected to obey. Like likelihood, it may by some be regarded as just another type of probability, a kind of prior probability this time; but in my view the distinction between it and likelihood, like that between likelihood and probability, is worth preserving. There are many unsolved problems in this direction.

DR D. R. COX

Some of the consequences of basing the formal theory of statistical inference and decision systematically on Bayes's theorem would be:

(i) the more or less automatic formal solution of parametric questions, including not only ones like the Fisher-Behrens problem, but also problems containing what would normally be regarded as non-identifiable parameters;

(ii) the theory of standard procedures, such as those based on the t and F distributions, could be developed very simply as corresponding to certain very special prior distributions. This would avoid the rather elaborate methods needed, for example, to obtain the t test as an optimum test in the Neyman-Pearson sense;

(iii) a single set of 'laws' would govern frequency ratios and measures of uncertainty;

(iv) certain complications in the conventional theory, such as the need to consider the stopping rule when analysing observations, would disappear.

D

In discussing the use of Bayes's theorem, when no prior *frequency* distribution is available, we need first to distinguish sharply between the approach based on subjective probability and the 'objective' or 'necessary' theory of Jeffreys (1948). Professor Savage has himself stressed this distinction. Although much of the mathematics is the same in the two theories, the meaning of the answers is entirely different. The following comments refer mainly to the subjective approach.

A decision about what to do in a given situation, whether in science or technology, does seem always to involve subjective considerations: quite apart from the assessment of sampling errors there are the often much more important doubts about interpretation and, in techno-logical matters, such things as whether conditions in the future will be at all like they have been in the past. If one wants to represent all this uncertainty in a formal mathematical scheme, the personalistic approach seems to me the way to do it.

An excellent reference on the subjective element in scientific research is the book by Beveridge (1951). He emphasizes, for instance, the subjective considerations connected with following up apparently fortuitous occurrences, such as that leading to the discovery of X-rays.

Statistical methods are, however, usually applied to very much narrower questions. We are interested in an unknown parameter of a frequency distribution and wish to consider questions about the parameter in the light of statistical data (i.e. data with stable fre-quencies). We are dealing then with a much more restricted problem and one to which a nearly impersonal quantitative answer is given by conventional methods of measuring uncertainty. Thus if a positive difference between a treated group and a control group is obtained, significant at the 0·1 per cent level, anyone wishing to deny the existence of a positive treatment effect must either

(i) say that by chance there is an exceptionally misleading result; or

(ii) say that there is an error in the design or execution of the experiment; or

(iii) say that the statistical analysis is inappropriate.

This usually narrows down the subjective element in the interpretation greatly; there may be disagreement between individuals over (ii) and (iii), but any such disagreement is open to rational discussion. The approach to such a problem by Bayes's theorem with a personal prior distribution leads in a sense to an answer to a more ambitious question. But the answer will vary from person to person and for one person from one time to another. In some, although of course by no means all, applications of statistics the near-objectivity of the answer is of great value. The disagreement between conventional and personalistic approaches seems to be one of tactics; at which stage the subjective considerations should be introduced.

When there is a marked difference between the Bayesian and non-Bayesian answers to a problem, the difference can often be traced to a difference in the attitude to unknown parameters. The unknown parameters may be those of direct concern or may be nuisance parameters. An extreme case is when we ask questions about a non-identifiable parameter θ. The Neyman-Pearson or Fisherian theories, which require that the measures of uncertainty (significance levels, etc.) should have a frequency interpretation whatever may be the values of the nuisance parameters, will say that no inference about θ is possible. If, however, we introduce a subjective prior probability distribution for the unknown parameters we can form a posterior distribution for θ, although this will of course be diffuse unless strong prior information about θ is fed in.

In general, the statements 'θ has some particular prior distribution $p(\theta)$ over the interval I' and 'θ may take on any value in the interval I' are qualitatively different in the following sense. It may turn out to be very important whether or not θ lies in some small subinterval; the first statement says that this is unlikely, the second does not. Of course, in many cases, especially if there is an appreciable amount of information in the data about θ, the introduction of the prior distribution is fairly harmless, and these are the solutions in which Bayesian and conventional answers agree closely numerically.

It may be useful to distinguish between the following types of conventional statistical argument in which explicit probabilistic aspects are important.

A. Assessment of evidence about statistical parameters. This type can be much subdivided.

B. Decision procedures with (nearly) objective loss functions and prior frequency distributions.

C. Decision procedures of the (α, β) type in which losses and prior probabilities do not enter quantitatively, but are considered qualitatively in choosing the appropriate probability of error of the first kind, α.

D. Decision procedures of type C with α chosen arbitrarily to be a conventional value such as 0·05.

There follow some miscellaneous comments on A–D.

(i) The difference between A and C is typified by the approach to standard significance tests. In A we give the level attained, in C and D we fix an α and use a rigid decision rule for 'acceptance' and 'rejection'.

(ii) C is very useful in those common situations in which something like a routine decision rule must be given but in which quantitative knowledge of costs is not available. The resulting rule may not be optimum, but has the substantial merit of having known properties, making rational discussion of different rules easier.

(iii) Significance tests in the sense of A are appropriate in at least two different situations, to

(a) measure evidence against a null hypothesis that is thought quite possibly to be nearly true;

(b) measure whether the direction of an effect has been reasonably well established, there being no particular reason for expecting the true value to be near null value.

In many practical applications (b) seems the more appropriate; much current criticism of significance tests overlooks this.

(iv) In thinking about significance tests, the Neyman-Pearson interpretation of α is kept in mind as a hypothetical procedure. Some minor difficulties in the Neyman-Pearson theory disappear; for example, the use of equi-tailed tests in two-sided situations can be justified from A, whereas in C equal tails are not usually appropriate.

(v) D, using an arbitrary conventional level of α and ignoring losses and prior probabilities, seems objectionable; as an approximation to A it may not be so bad.

To sum up, a key issue seems to me to be the following. Do we have an approach of limited scope, in which all probabilities have a frequency interpretation, in which our answers are nearly objective, but in which personal judgement has to be introduced qualitatively in making use of the answers? Or do we take an approach which appears to take us quantitatively further, but in which our answers are subjective and often difficult to specify numerically at all precisely? At present I favour the first approach, especially where it is important to convey to other people the statistical uncertainty in the conclusions.

A final general comment is that the discussion above is of the question of how to reach conclusions about parameters in a model on which we are agreed. It seems to me, however, that a more important matter is how to formulate more realistic models that will enable scientifically more searching questions to be asked of data.

PROFESSOR E. S. PEARSON

Of the previous speakers, I suppose that I am in most general agreement with Professor Bartlett, but at the same time I have a natural sympathy with anyone who is trying to thrash out better ways of handling the problems of statistical inference. Professor Savage has spoken of the enthusiasm with which he sees new lines of thought being opened out in front of him, and perhaps I had somewhat the same feelings round about 1931 when I visited the U.S. and discussed ideas which seemed to be opening out in front of Neyman and myself.

There were a good many references in the previous contributions to the Neyman and Pearson theory; they did not altogether correspond to the theory as I see it, but that perhaps is because my own views have changed somewhat and developed. Of course, through lack of close contact with my partner during the last twenty years, it would be a little difficult to say where precisely the N. and P. theory stands today! I think, however, that a few words on past history may not be out of place, because I believe in the value of emphasizing the continuity as well as the differences in what have been the broad lines of development of our subject. I have the impression that by showing how the same situation is being tackled by alternative approaches the whole subject gains in richness in a way it would not if the exponents of one line set out to discredit another line by saying it was followed in error!

There has perhaps been a tendency to speak of the Neyman-Pearson contribution as some static theory, rather than as part of the process of development of our thought on the background of statistical theory. N. and P. were after all very much persons of their time. They built on things which they found in the middle 1920's. For example:

(a) The way of thinking which had found acceptance for a number of years among practising statisticians, which included the use of tail areas of the distributions of test statistics.

(b) The classical tradition that somehow prior probabilities should be introduced numerically into a solution. Perhaps only lip service was still being paid to this idea, but one can certainly find some evidence for the strength of the tradition in certain of the writings of Karl Pearson and of 'Student'.

(c) The tremendous impact of R. A. Fisher; his criticism of Bayes's Theorem and his use of Likelihood.

(d) Fisher's geometrical presentation, which first came home to me in the small diagram in his paper on the distribution of a correlation coefficient (Fisher, 1915, p. 509). Out of this readily came the concept of alternative 'critical regions' in a sample space.

(e) Fisher's tables of 5 per cent and 1 per cent significance levels, which lent themselves to the idea of a choice, in advance of experimentation, of the risk which the experimenter was prepared to take of the 'first kind of error'.

(f) The emphasis on the importance of planning an experiment, which leads naturally to the examination of a power function, both in choosing the size of sample to enable worthwhile results to be achieved and in determining the most appropriate test.

(g) Then too there were contributions from 'Student', some of them from personal discussion; I remember particularly his letter to me of 1926 which helped to put the concept of the alternative hypothesis into the picture.

What I think we found, as no doubt Savage and others think that they find now, was a dissatisfaction with the logical basis, or lack of it, which seemed to underly the choice and development of statistical tests. We found this not only in the theoretical work of what was then called the Biometric school but also to some extent in R. A. Fisher's work, as far as we could understand his underlying philosophy. We tried therefore to find a set of principles with a mathematical basis which it seemed to us would lead to a rational choice of statistical procedures when faced with certain types of problem in the analysis of data. Put in another way, we were seeking how to bring probability theory into gear with the way we think – or, you may like to say, the way we thought we think, for it is a rather difficult problem for anyone to nail down just how he does think. No doubt, because the scope of application of statistical methods in those days was narrower, the emphasis which we gave to certain types of situation may now seem out of balance.

We were certainly aware that inferences must make use of prior information and that decisions must also take account of utilities, but after some considerable thought and discussion round these points we came to the conclusion, rightly or wrongly, that it was so rarely possible to give sure numerical values to these entities that our line of approach must proceed otherwise. Thus we came down on the side of using only probability measures which could be related to relative frequency. I think I am right in saying that it was Neyman, brought up in the continental mathematical school, who held longest to the idea of retaining in our theory measures of prior probability. You will find that in his paper which gave the first exposition in English of confidence interval theory (Neyman, 1934, pp. 589–93), a function representing a prior probability distribution appears, although it is shown that knowledge of its value is in that problem immaterial. Again, in another paper (Neyman and Pearson, 1933) we discussed 'the testing of statistical hypotheses in relation to probabilities *a priori*'. Just because the problem of specifying the numerical values of these probabilities seemed to us so often insoluble, our aim here was to discuss in what sense the conclusions drawn from a test could be described as independent of these probabilities.

We also considered how far inferences and decisions could be based on the numerical values of likelihood ratios. But while we first obtained the critical or rejection regions of our theory as the contours in the sample space on which the appropriate likelihood ratio was constant, we thought that the meaning of a test was more easily grasped if expressed in terms of the integral of the probability density inside (or beyond) the boundary of the region, rather than in terms of the likelihood ratio on the boundary.

Thus it seems to me that Professor Savage, and Professor Barnard, are again at the same points, but with new arguments which in their view lead to different conclusions from ours. I think to a large extent we are or were trying to meet the same requirements of a 'rational man' in different ways, and to me at any rate it will be illuminating to explore the parallelism further than has so far been done. The personal probability which Professor Savage expresses in so far as he can in numerical measure, using, if I understand correctly, the analogy of betting odds, is undoubtedly paralleled by my own conception of the need for the exercise of personal judgement in such matters as choosing the appropriate significance level or trying to decide on the magnitude of a worthwhile effect or on the balance of utilities. I have little doubt that when expressed in a variety of situations, where possible in numerical terms, the composition of Professor Savage's expressions for the posterior estimation of odds will throw light on the different facets of the more intuitive process of personal judgement to which the 'frequentist' must appeal.

But to throw illumination on one approach by comparison with another is not the same thing as to substitute one approach for the other. I would hope somehow to reach a blend of the two! My own personal difficulty is that there seem to be so many situations in which I cannot imagine how I would assign numerical values which would satisfy me to prior probabilities and utilities. The number of matters to be taken into account under the heading of prior information seems to be so vast. There are not only the prior distributions for μ and σ, but for normality, for equality of variance, for the degree of homogeneity of the data and its randomness. In the questions of utility it seems to me that we are often not faced with straight economic comparisons; how, for example, as occurs in medical research, are we to balance in precise numerical terms the possible chance of saving life against the waste of a limited supply of experimental effort?

If the complete formulation, even in algebraic terms, of all the factors which in some way influence human judgement is not possible it seems that the new theory cannot be mathematically complete as a model of the working of the human mind. It may in fact be that what it will lead to, for the practising statistician, is the use of old tools with a new understanding and confidence. Possibly Professor Savage is not yet prepared to say what he hopes for in this direction himself? At any rate, what I feel quite sure at the moment to be needed is simple illustration of the new notions on real, everyday statistical problems. Until this is attempted, the matter rests largely on the plane of academic discussion.

There are two small points which previous speakers made on which I should like to comment.

Professor Barnard introduced the idea of a 'simple test of significance' where there was no specified alternative and quoted the problem of Daniel Bernoulli regarding the orbits of the planets as the first example of the application of such a test of which he was aware. The null hypothesis was that the poles of the orbits of the six major planets* were randomly and uniformly distributed over a sphere. The test which Bernoulli used shows that he had in mind, whether consciously or not, alternatives which suggested that the poles had been restrained, through some unknown factors, to lie within a small area. Had an alternative to randomness involved some idea of a repulsive force acting between the poles, the test he would have used would surely have been quite different? As I see it, the concept that a test can only be chosen rationally having regard to the likely class of alternatives, is relevant whether or not the alternatives can be assigned in physical terms and given a precise mathematical specification. To derive an 'optimum' test it may be necessary to have a shot at formally specifying the alternatives mathematically, but I think that the notion of alternatives can guide our procedure in a rational way without precise mathematical specification.

Later Dr Cox spoke of the advantage of using prior distributions from the point of view of simplicity in teaching as compared with elaborate considerations of power. But I think this is only a question of the teacher and how he introduces his subject. It is always difficult for us to be sure how far our students really understand what we say, but it never seems to me difficult to present and illustrate simple ideas of power in the first term or two of a statistical course. On the other

* Six major planets, including Earth, were known in 1734.

hand, the introduction of prior distributions seems to me much more difficult because of the impossibility, in illustration, of putting forward with conviction a meaningful distribution with parameters having assigned numerical values.

DR C. A. B. SMITH

I have two apologies to make. Firstly, I may repeat what is already well known through not being aware of all the latest developments. Secondly, I may appear to be rude to various members of the conference. This is not intended to be either arrogant, or dogmatic, or unfriendly to those who know much more about these things than I do: it is simply that I am trying to put the points briefly.

I will soon have to give some general account of statistics to biologists, and this has compelled some thought on the fundamentals of the subject, which has reinforced some long-standing uneasiness.

(a) The general standard of self-criticism among statisticians seems to be too low in certain aspects, although in other ways (e.g. in the mathematics) it is very high. Thus, statistical procedures generally depend on certain assumptions, such as normality of distributions, or equality of variances. In fact, in some cases these assumptions matter little, in other cases they make an appreciable difference, and in others they are quite critical. For example, in a 2 by 2 block experiment,

	not-N	N
not-P	x	y
P	z	w

where x, y, z, w represent the responses, when we are finding the standard error of the main effects of N and of P and the interaction, it is of no importance whether the variances of x, y, z and w are equal or not, since the standard errors depend only on the average of the four variances. If, however, we are interested in the variance of the effect of N in the absence of P, the question of equality does matter, since if x and y have much smaller variances than z and w, the average will overestimate the variance of $x - y$.

Of course, we know that much work has been done on the effect of non-normality on the t distribution, on robust tests, etc. Also, in some cases experts may know by long experience that the assumptions are fulfilled. Generally, however, such assumptions are allowed to go with relatively little challenge, especially in textbooks. In almost any other science, any such basic assumptions would be vigorously questioned and the investigator required to produce compelling justification.

I might add that while I know little about field experiments, in the type of biological material I am familiar with, there are often quite striking differences in variance.

(b) Statisticians often play down something which is obviously true, when it does not quite accord with their line of thought. An example is the statement that there is no difference between inference and decision problems.

A decision problem means the choice between several possible courses of action: this will have observable consequences, which may be used to test its rightness. An inference concerns the degree of belief, which need not have any consequences, though it may. This makes it more difficult to come to agreement on questions of inference than on decisions. For example, the question 'Shall I eat this apple?' is a matter of decision, with possible highly satisfactory or uncomfortable outcomes: 'Is this apple green?' is a question of belief. Of course, the two problems must be closely related, even though they are distinct: if one accepts Professor Savage's theory, the decisions are closely related to the probabilities by the rule of maximizing expected utility.

Another similar untruth is the assertion that frequency probability is a particular case of subjective probability. This may be formally true, just as it is formally true that an integer is a particular case of a rational number. However, a frequency is measurable (apart from slight difficulties about convergence to the limit): a subjective probability is only ideally measurable.*

(c) What has Professor Savage done? A 'consistent' man is one who obeys a few axioms of the type: 'If I prefer A to B, and B to C, then I do not prefer C to A.'

* Note added later: Both frequency and subjective probability are properly considered as fictions, as Dr Good subsequently remarked: they are, however, rather different fictions, it seems to me.

The reasonableness of such axioms can readily be seen by considering them in practical situations, e.g. let A = strawberries and cream, B = bread and butter, C = stale cheese. If the axiom was untrue, I could make no choice when asked to choose one out of the three, since whatever choice I made, another would seem preferable. This is absurd.

It seems that if one makes a few such axioms, which could scarcely be disputed by any reasonable person, one can show that anyone who is consistent in this sense *must* behave as if he had measurable prior probabilities and utilities. There is no loophole of escape, as far as I can see at the moment. It applies to the major decisions of life as well as to the minor recurring ones.

Such an absolutely consistent person does not, of course, exist. Consistency is not *necessarily* a virtue: one can be consistently obnoxious. However, inconsistency is not necessarily a virtue either, and it seems reasonable to try to make a theory of probability consistent in this sense, i.e. to make it agree with Professor Savage's theory, at least unless there is some very compelling reason why one should do otherwise in any particular circumstances.

(*d*) Significance tests, in their usual form, are not compatible with a Bayesian attitude. However, they have certain virtues, in that they reduce the data to a single number, the significance level, which is 'objective' in the sense that all statisticians would agree on it, and is easily grasped in a way that a whole series of numbers or graph is not. In principle, one should give the likelihood function as the result of an experiment, but it is often convenient to try to get some single number summarizing the data.

This could be done as follows. As an example, suppose we wish to test whether some probability p is $\frac{1}{2}$ or not. The appropriate method is to give some initial probability A that $p = \frac{1}{2}$, and distribute the remaining probability $1 - A$ over the remaining values of p. However, it will usually make no important difference if the remaining probability is uniformly distributed between 0 and 1: this redistribution may change the final probabilities by a small factor, but not so much as to seriously alter any conclusions which may be drawn. We then have in the usual way that

$$\text{Final odds} = \text{initial odds} \times \text{likelihood ratio,}$$

where the initial odds, $A/(1-A)$, are a measure of one's general prejudice in favour of the null hypothesis $p = \frac{1}{2}$, and the likelihood ratio is calculated for the two distributions (i) $p = \frac{1}{2}$, (ii) p uniformly distributed between 0 and 1. Thus it seems eminently reasonable to summarize the data by the likelihood ratio: anyone can weight this by whatever value of $A/(1-A)$ he feels reasonable before drawing his own conclusions. Good and Jeffreys mention very similar procedures.

(e) It seems to me, however, that most significance tests used in practice should really be estimation problems. We do not wish to know whether some treatment has any effect – it almost certainly has – but only what is the magnitude of this effect, if appreciable, or whether it is positive or negative.

PART III

Discussion

Professor L. J. S A V A G E*: I keenly appreciate the patient, competent, and understanding atmosphere in which subjective probability is being discussed here. For example, Dr Smith, in section (c) of his talk, skilfully underlines an important point, namely this. The theory of subjective probability describes ideally consistent behaviour and ought not, therefore, be taken too literally. But there is evidence that today this particular idealization is a promising one for statistics.

The comments I shall make just now are mainly stimulated by Professor Pearson's talk, which seemed particularly important and representative.

It is disadvantageous to use the names of contemporaries to designate views and theories. In intellectual, as opposed to historical and biographical discussion, what particular individuals think is difficult to determine but of infinitesimal importance, and what they used to think ought to be an infinitesimal of higher order. In particular, what I, and many other statisticians, call the Neyman-Pearson view may, for all I know, never have been held by Professor Neyman or by Professor Pearson, but it is a view widespread among other statistical theorists, especially in America, but also here in England, in India, and elsewhere. A work excellently representing this view is Lehmann's (1959) book on testing hypotheses.

If the theory of subjective probability does have a contribution to make to statistics, it is as an addition to, not a substitute for, the past half-century of rapid progress, as Professor Pearson wisely emphasized. Indeed, the new ideas could hardly have arisen but for the traditions to which we statisticians have been exposed. For example, though de Finetti has a wider and deeper knowledge and understanding of the philosophy of probability than anyone else I know, he is not

* Professor Savage was invited to open the discussion by commenting on the contributions in Part II.

close to statistical literature and practice and is therefore without a certain stimulus that we statisticians give each other.

It is illuminating, and somewhat germane to Professor Pearson's talk, to reflect on the idea of choosing a power function from among those available. Once a specific model is accepted – and we all realize that this acceptance must not be too literal – there is fair general agreement that the power function (or perhaps more generally, operating characteristic) fully describes an experiment together with its statistical analysis. To decide what experiment to do and how to analyse it amounts schematically to choosing one among the many available power functions. Incidentally, when the experiment as well as the design is being chosen, each power function has its price to be taken into account. Excessive attention to the tautology that many problems of statistics are tantamount to choosing one among the set of available power functions has, I believe, interfered with our seeing an important road that leads through the objectivistic terrain to the theory of subjective probability.

The situation is greatly clarified by the study of simple dichotomies. However rarely we meet simple dichotomies in nature, I ask you to feel with me that they are statistics in microcosm. For all that I am about to say can be generalized directly to problems about any finite number of simple hypotheses and any finite number of conclusions or decisions; nor do infinite sets present any unusual difficulties. The programme is to talk about simple dichotomies in the prevailing, extra-Bayesian, spirit so far as possible and thus to bring out clearly where and to what extent subjective probability enters as a step forward.

Suppose then that one of two facts, f_0 or f_1, is the case. A wealth of experiments relevant to deciding between f_0 and f_1 is available to you, and each of these experiments will ordinarily admit a wealth of analyses. You must, in this particular hypothetical example, choose one of two actions, one of which is appropriate to f_0 and the other to f_1. Thus, an analysis is simply a region of acceptance for f_0. The available experiments would typically have various costs, but for a simple first approach suppose that they cost you nothing or, which comes to much the same thing, that they all cost the same. It is traditional, and I think correct, to say that your choice is a choice of one of the available power functions. Here a power function is simply a pair of numbers (α, β), the probabilities of errors of the first and second kind. There seems to be agreement that your choice among the available pairs (α, β) must be made subjectively. It is true that the minimax theory adduces a choice among the available pairs from cost considerations alone, but it is not hard to see that this is a quite unreasonable theory for simple dichotomies.

Consider a graphical representation of the unit square of all pairs of errors (α, β). As is implicit in the idea of the errors of the first and second kind, no one wants to exchange a given position in this square for any position to the north-east of it; this expresses the principle of admissibility. The points in the square made available by any one experiment typically consist of a convex set connecting the two corners $(1, 0)$ and $(0, 1)$. The south-west boundary of the convex set is a curve connecting these two corners, and if you were confined to the set, you would surely choose some point on its south-west boundary, as the principle of admissibility requires. According to the Neyman-Pearson lemma, these admissible tests are exactly the likelihood-ratio tests. The critical likelihood ratio in favour of f_1 that gives rise to the likelihood-ratio test corresponding to a given point on the south-west curve is simply the negative of the slope of the curve at this point. This interesting and important fact is easy to verify.

At this stage, it is traditional to conclude thus: Given the experiment, the person will simply have to choose whichever critical likelihood ratio results in the (α, β) pair that pleases him most among those available. Sometimes a little guidance is suggested to the effect that the person might like to require α to be a hundredth, or a twentieth, letting β then fall where it may. Presumably no one would vigorously defend this rule, so in practice, no firm advice beyond the principle of admissibility is generally offered for choosing among the available pairs (α, β). But Mr Lindley and I convinced ourselves several years ago that much more can be done, as will now be explained.

Turning back temporarily, let us think about your preferences among the points in the (α, β)-square, in connection with some specific problem of choice. If P_1 is south-west of P_2, then you will prefer P_1; and no one can dispute any particular preference that does not violate this rule. Presumably, your preferences could be described by a system of indifference curves in the (α, β)-square like those for various combinations of bread and wine in the economics classroom. So far as bread and wine are concerned, indifference curves are notoriously highly arbitrary families of curves that reflect a vast latitude for possible subjective differences in preference. It is natural to leap to the conclusion that your indifference curves for points in the (α, β)-square are equally arbitrary. For example, Lehmann (1958) does accept that conclusion with its discouraging implications.

Fortunately, pairs of error probabilities are quite different from quantities of bread and wine. Suppose, for example, that you found yourself indifferent between one test and analysis culminating in the point P_1 and another test and analysis culminating in P_2. Being indifferent, surely you would not mind if someone else chose between these two procedures for you, and if he chose with the aid of a table of random numbers, that too should be indifferent to you. But to choose between these two procedures at random, with a specified probability, is, in effect, to create a third procedure with the error-pair P_3 on the line segment from P_1 to P_2. Thus if P_1 is indifferent to P_2 for you, then all of the points on the segment between them are too. Similar considerations of coherence culminate in the conclusion that your indifference curves must be parallel straight lines; nothing is left to your discretion save the choice of one number, the slope of these lines. This slope is simply the rate at which you are willing to increase β per unit decrease in α. In summary, your preferences among pairs are largely subjective, but this subjective choice is not nearly so complex as one might have thought; all is reduced to the choice of a slope or rate of exchange. Everything said here in the name of simple dichotomies admits great generalization. In particular, where a procedure can be expressed in terms of many conditional probabilities of error rather than of two only, preference among these patterns is governed simply by constant rates of exchange, and the indifference loci are parallel linear manifolds.

To mention an important criticism emphasized by Professor Pearson, you may find it hard in practice adequately to specify the slope that applies in a given problem, but the difficulty of a choice does not make it escapable. Any decision you make will amount to a decision about your critical slope. Fortunately, you may not be called upon, in any one problem, to fix the slope with much precision. As

E

will be explained later, you often need specify your rate of exchange only to within a factor of 5, 10, or even 100.

Suppose now that you have approximately fixed your critical slope, and return to the problem of choosing a point on the south-west boundary of the set of error pairs made available by a fixed experiment, that is, choosing a likelihood-ratio test. If you draw a sketch showing your parallel straight indifference curves and the convex curve connecting (1, 0) and (0, 1) that represents the family of all likelihood-ratio tests, the best likelihood-ratio test for you is plainly the one represented by the point where the south-west curve has for its slope your critical slope. This means that you prefer, no matter what the experiment was, to base a likelihood-ratio test on a critical likelihood ratio equal to minus your critical slope. If, for example, someone were to make available a larger experiment than the one originally envisaged, you would continue to use the same critical likelihood ratio, so your new preferred (α, β), except for being smaller, would have no necessary relation to the old pair. In practice you may have quite a broad and diffuse interval of likelihood ratios that would leave you uncomfortable in making a decision. But, especially if the experiment is fairly large, there is a good chance that the outcome would not fall within the border zone. Also, practical relief could come from the possibility of further experimentation or some other kind of hedging.

Of course, had we started out as Bayesians with utilities and subjective probabilities, we would have arrived at the conclusion about a critical slope immediately. Indeed, the derivation of the critical slope that I have sketched is, in effect, a derivation of subjective probabilities suitable for one who takes objective probabilities for granted but is sceptical of subjective ones. To sum up, not only for simple dichotomies, but for all problems involving choice of power function or operating characteristic, any coherent system of choices will be governed by a critical likelihood ratio (or system of ratios). This system of critical likelihood ratios, in the presence of a definite cost structure, amounts to a subjective probability distribution. This prior distribution pertains to the whole ensemble of conceivable experiments bearing on a given issue, unlike the idea of a critical α and β for a specific experiment. There is, I feel, an important step forward here, and it does not depend on anyone's ability really to name his subjective probabilities in detail. Noticing the strong arguments in favour of parallel, linear loci surely is not a step backward. When you ask yourself, as these arguments lead you to, how much more probable you consider f_0 than f_1, you are focusing on something that has strong intuitive meaning and is not complicated by the particular experiment at hand. Whereas, if you ask yourself, as it seems to me statistical theory has for a long time insisted you do, which point on a particular south-west boundary you prefer, your choice is no less subjective and difficult, and a needless element of complication and confusion has been introduced.

It has been aptly said that the subjectivist's position is more objective than the objectivist's, for the subjectivist finds the range of coherent or reasonable preference patterns much narrower than the objectivist thought it to be. How confusing and dangerous big words are!

If your problem is not to make a dichotomous decision but rather to say how some experiment already performed bears on whether it is f_0 or f_1 that obtains, then, according to some tradition, the α or β (or both) of that likelihood-ratio test for which the experiment is just marginal would constitute a good summary. But, in the Bayesian view, this likelihood-ratio itself is a thorough summary, while the corresponding (α, β) is not.

Dr H. RUBEN: Professor Savage has criticized Stein's two-stage sampling procedure. I certainly agree with these criticisms, and in fact made similar ones from a non-Bayesian point of view in a dissertation in 1950. The difficulty of the problem appears to arise from the perhaps artificial objective of controlling the length of the confidence interval absolutely rather than stochastically. It is, however, possible to modify the procedure so that the objections are to a considerable extent met.

Suppose that it is required to obtain confidence intervals of width $2a$ for the mean. Let $\bar{x}$ be the sample mean at the end of Stein's procedure and denote by $P(\sigma)$ the true confidence coefficient, as a function of σ, of the interval $(\bar{x} - a, \bar{x} + a)$. Then it is highly likely that $P(\sigma)$ is a decreasing function of σ. One may estimate say an upper limit to σ from *all* the data, and thereby obtain an estimated confidence coefficient that is in a sense better than Stein's nominal confidence coefficient in which information about σ contained in the second sample is rejected.

Professor G. A. BARNARD: As I understand it, Professor Savage is prepared to accept that the probabilities which enter into the likelihood factor in Bayes's theorem are commonly known with greater precision than the probabilities which enter into the prior distribution. It might, therefore, if this is accepted, generally be advisable to distinguish these first probabilities by calling them likelihoods, as opposed to the probabilities entering into the prior factor which might be called prior probabilities or some other name, such as acceptibilities, plausibilities, etc. Does he agree?

SAVAGE: It seems to me that Professor Barnard is calling attention to the need for two apt names. First there is the probability of a datum given a hypothesis (or parameter value), regardless of whether this probability is public or private, or clear or vague. I would not call these probabilities likelihoods, simply because 'likelihood' is preempted in my usage and that of many others for something a little different. Perhaps 'structural probability' would be a good expression for the probability of a datum given a parameter value.

A word for probabilities that are relatively sharp and public as structural probabilities usually are is also needed, but not one suggesting that such probabilities are necessarily different in principle from more vague and more private ones. Perhaps something like 'model probability' would serve.

Professor M. S. BARTLETT: I agree with Professor Savage that it would be useful to have a new name, and of course in the literature there have been different symbols. For example, Carnap has used what substantially amounts to the same sort of distinction as here, using p_1 and p_2 for two kinds of probability. Writing quite a long time ago in discussing some of Jeffreys's work, I used P for degrees of belief, and p for probabilities appearing as statistical probabilities or chances, over which there was complete agreement.

Dr I. J. GOOD: It seems to me that one set of probabilities are tautological probabilities. They are probabilities whose values are assigned by *definition* of a statistical hypothesis.

SAVAGE: Of course, many discussions and calculations in which we use the word probability are pure mathematics – they are schematic only – even when they are done with a view to immediate application. But it is anything but tautological to say that the errors made by a particular balance are normally distributed around the true weights with an unknown variance. It takes a lot of judgement to make such a statement responsibly, and we all know that this judgement can easily be wrong.

BARNARD: Is it not a question of what we mean when we say that the posterior probability of A is such and such? Here A is the statement that certain events have certain probabilities, and this is really the starting point for the discussion. You may say that we agree that this balance has a normally distributed set of errors. If we do not agree with that, we do not know what we are talking about when we say that the probability of this parameter value is such and such; nor do you know what you mean when you say that the statement has a posterior probability of so and so. You must know what the statement means, as well as knowing what its probability is.

SAVAGE: Yes.

BARNARD: The point I am trying to make is that we are discussing the posterior probabilities of hypotheses. By hypotheses we mean statements which specify probabilities. There are two levels of probability, the level which appears in the hypothesis and the level when we talk about the posterior probability of the hypothesis. I am suggesting it would be worthwhile to distinguish these two levels by different names.

SAVAGE: I have the impression that you want me to discuss the meaning of such a proposition as this: 'The number of heads in the next thousand tosses of this coin is governed by a binomial distribution of unknown probability P.' According to the viewpoint that I have learned from de Finetti, this statement translates thus: 'I regard any sequence of heads and tails that this coin might produce as equiprobable for me with any permutation of the sequence.' Briefly, the tosses of the coin are 'exchangeable'.

I often prefer to use the original, perhaps misleading statement about unknown probabilities, because it is familiar and also because it reminds us of an important mathematical truth about exchangeable events. As de Finetti has pointed out, no one is so Copernican as to refrain from saying, 'The sun is rising.'

Incidentally, it is in view of de Finetti's analysis of exchangeable events that I think it unnecessary to seek a theory of frequency probability. Whether such a search has succeeded or will succeed is still another question. But anyone who thinks that a frequency theory of probability is called for by common sense should at least familiarize himself with the elements of the theory of exchangeable events. An introduction is given in my book (Savage, 1954, section 3.7). The main reference is de Finetti (1937), and a relatively new and mathematically fancy reference is Hewitt and Savage (1955).

BARNARD: Can we agree that when the prior probabilities are smooth, your posterior probabilities are what many of us call likelihoods, and behave in mathematically the same way?

SAVAGE: When the prior probabilities are smooth, in the right sense, a good approximate posterior distribution is the normalized likelihood function. But, in an ordinary estimation of a variance, for example, one might feel that σ^2 times the prior density of σ^2 is the function that is smooth. This is analogous to Jeffreys's policy of taking the logarithm of σ^2 rather than σ^2 itself to be uniformly distributed. In such a case, the natural approximate posterior distribution is not identical with the likelihood. For my own part, even where the two happen to be the same in fact, I prefer to think of them as conceptually different.

BARNARD: One reason for the difference is that you phrase Bayes's theorem in the form of proportionality. To get the likelihood to add up to one you divide by the proportionality factor; you can always do that if you want to.

GOOD: Since a previous speaker has described subjective probabilities as 'metaphysical' I should like to say that all probabilities seem to me to some extent metaphysical. That is to say that in all cases, whatever type of probability we care to use, we behave and talk *as if* these things existed. This applies both to subjective probabilities and to physical probabilities. Most of us probably think about a biased coin as if it had a physical probability. Now whether it is defined in terms of frequency or just falls out of another type of theory, I think we do argue that way. I suspect that even the most extreme subjectivist such as de Finetti would have to agree that he did sometimes think that way, though he would perhaps avoid doing it in print. I do not think there is all that much distinction between the metaphysical status of subjective and physical probabilities. You can arrive at the numerical value of a physical probability by means of a repeated experiment in which you gradually modify the subjective probability and in that way you can measure your physical probability in terms of subjective probabilities.

Savage has shown that a rational man behaves as if he used subjective probabilities. A rational man will also presumably behave as if he thought the world behaves as if there are physical probabilities. When he measures these physical probabilities he will behave as if they were limiting values of his subjective probabilities. Thus both types of probability are metaphysical, and perhaps everything is. I mean we use language and behave *as if* we had various opinions.

Mr D. V. LINDLEY: I think we ought to look carefully at the situations that the subjectivist seems to analyse differently from the way that most of us have been taught to use. One of these situations, described by Professor Savage in Part I, concerns optional stopping. He gave a very pertinent discussion of what happens when we have six successes out of a hundred. I am disappointed that none of the other speakers has been tempted to reply to this, to say whether he would agree with Professor Savage or not. Is there for instance someone who feels that he wants to use estimates that take account of the stopping rule?

BARTLETT: I am not going to answer the question completely, but there is one small point I should like to make. Certainly I agree that unbiased estimates are unimportant. And in the particular problem, I have pointed out before if you have six successes out of a hundred in an ordinary fixed-sample-size situation, you take $6/100$ as the sufficient statistic that happens to be unbiased and carries the maximum information. If you have inverse sampling, it seems to me that certainly you should take $100/6$ as your unbiased estimate of $1/p$, which is sufficient and carries the maximum information in the inverse sampling case. You have to take 5/99 to get an unbiased estimate of p. I should like to think about the general question further though.

DR P. ARMITAGE: I think it is quite clear that likelihood ratios, and therefore posterior probabilities, do not depend on a stopping rule. Professor Savage, Dr Cox and Mr Lindley take this necessarily as a point in favour of the use of Bayesian methods. My own feeling goes the other way. I feel that if a man deliberately stopped an investigation when he had departed sufficiently far from his particular hypothesis, then 'Thou shalt be misled if thou dost not know that'. If so, prior probability methods seem to appear in a less attractive light than frequency methods, where one can take into account the method of sampling. I should like Professor Savage to clarify a point he made in Part I. He remarked that, using conventional significance tests, if you go on long enough you can be sure of achieving any level of significance; does not the same sort of result happen with Bayesian methods? The departure of the mean by two standard errors corresponds to the ordinary five per cent level. It also corresponds to the null hypothesis being at the five per cent point of the posterior distribution. Does it not follow that by going on sufficiently long one can be sure of getting the null value arbitrarily far into the tail of the posterior distribution?

SAVAGE: The answer is surely no, under any interpretation. It is impossible to be sure of sampling until the data justifies an unjustifiable conclusion, just as surely as it is impossible to build a perpetual-motion machine. After all, whatever we may disagree about, we are surely agreed that Bayes's theorem is true where it applies. But to understand this impossibility let us examine first a simple case.

Consider an urn that contains three red balls and a black one or three black balls and a red one. To convince you of the first hypothesis as opposed to the second, for some given purpose, would mean to make the likelihood ratio in favour of the first sufficiently large, say at least 10. Suppose that I, in my zeal, decide to keep sampling (with replacement) until the likelihood ratio, which in this particular case is 3^{r-b}, exceeds 10. This will happen if and only if I sometimes succeed in drawing three more red balls than black ones; if there are really three black balls and a red one, it is quite probable that I never will succeed until the end of time. In fact, the probability of failure in this unfavourable circumstance is at least 9/10, as it ought to be on general principles; the exact value is 26/27.

As I understand it, Dr Armitage is particularly interested in the following sort of example. The prior distribution of a parameter μ is rather broadly distributed around 0, and observations of μ with unit standard deviation are sequentially available. From 'your' point of view, that is, the point of view summarized by the assumed prior distribution, what is the probability P that I should succeed in sampling until your posterior odds that μ is positive are at least 10 times your initial odds that μ is positive, if μ is in fact negative? There can be no escape from the simple general formula that P is at most a tenth, but there might be some momentary misunderstanding of the meaning of that formula.

If μ is not negative, and I sample with a determination to raise your odds in favour of the proposition that μ is positive by large factor, I am of course sure to succeed. Still more, if μ is only very slightly negative, then, with determination I am almost sure to succeed in convincing you that μ is positive. This may at first seem objectionable, but you must not forget that 'you' felt very sure at the outset that μ was not close to 0, so the general conclusion that you are not unduly likely to be fooled has not been upset.

If optional stopping is irrelevant to the analysis when we have well-defined probabilities to work with, ought we to expect it to affect a reasonable analysis of the data when the prior probabilities happen to be vague? No example strongly pointing toward an affirmative answer has yet been adduced.

Dr D. R. Cox: In the problem of the significance test, it seems to me that the Bayesian argument attains independence of the sampling rule by answering a somewhat different question from that we usually think about. Suppose that the null hypothesis is $\theta = 0$ and that we do some sort of optional stopping and end up with a very small $\bar{x}$ and a very large n. Now, as I understand the Bayesian point of view, the prior distribution must be fixed and independent of n; we have some prior probability at $\theta = 0$ and the remainder distributed in some way over the non-zero values of θ. If we ask the question 'Is θ zero or not?', we have in this case only two effective possibilities: either $\theta = 0$, or θ lies in a narrow band of width roughly $1/\sqrt{n}$ near 0. But the Bayes approach seems to me to have partly prejudged the issue by assigning very small prior probability to this latter band; it says that if θ is not zero, it is very unlikely to be in any particular narrow range. I think that putting in a prior distribution is causing us to answer a different question from 'Are or are not the data consistent with $\theta = 0$?' Now, of course, a further point often comes in that one says very small values of θ are practically unimportant and can be identified with the value of zero. That is a different issue. I think that the consideration of tail areas does enable us to deal with the question of consistency with a null hypothesis, without prejudging the issue by putting down a prior distribution that effectively excludes the possibility of a very small non-zero value of θ.

GOOD: A possible weakness in the use of the Bayes approach is in having a function which is smooth all the way to zero. It may be that the density function should tend to infinity, which in principle certainly comes closer to Dr Cox's case, so that after say, 10^{100} observations you would be able to say θ is very slightly different from zero. An assumption about a prior distribution that seems reasonable for a moderate size of experiment may not be advisable if you are going to do a very big experiment. You so to speak oversimplify because you know in advance that you are not going to do more than say a million experimental trials.

SAVAGE: What is essential to the Bayesian point of view, or approach, for the class of problem under discussion, is this. We believe that some prior distributions for the parameter θ will lead exclusively to beliefs and behaviour that you would regard as reasonable for the given situation. Since a tail area analysis, being in conflict with the likelihood principle, is not compatible with any prior distribution, and since the analogue of such an analysis is clearly contraindicated in exaggeratedly simple problems like simple dichotomy, we think it must be wrong.

To be sure, the particular kinds of prior distribution thus far mentioned in connection with hypothesis testing during this conference are not appropriate to all, or even to many, practical situations. Often, as you show, my actual prejudice against the parameter's lying near but not at the origin is less than a certain naïve model of my prior distribution would suggest, so that this model does not give a faithful image of my opinion in such a situation. To conclude from the inappropriateness of one kind of prior distribution that we should take seriously a procedure incompatible with all prior distributions seems to me to go further than is justified. The Bayesian theory does not yet have models of all, or even most, of the situations traditionally treated by hypothesis testing, but better analyses have not, to my knowledge, been demonstrated outside of Bayesian statistics.

BARNARD: I have been made to think further about this issue of the stopping rule since I first suggested that the stopping rule was irrelevant (Barnard, 1947a, b). This conclusion does not follow only from the subjective theory of probability; it seems to me that the stopping rule is irrelevant *in certain circumstances*. Since 1947 I have had the great benefit of a long correspondence – not many letters because they were not very frequent, but it went on over a long time – with Professor Bartlett, as a result of which I am considerably clearer than I was before. My feeling is that, as I indicated [on p. 42], we meet with two sorts of situation in applying statistics to data. One is where we want to have a single hypothesis with which to confront the data. Do they agree with this hypothesis or do they not? Now in that situation you cannot apply Bayes's theorem because you have not got any alternatives to think about and specify – not yet. I do not say they are not specifiable – they are not specified yet. And in that situation it seems to me the stopping rule is relevant.

In particular, suppose somebody sets out to demonstrate the existence of extrasensory perception and says 'I am going to go on until I get a one in ten thousand significance level'. Knowing that this is what he is setting out to do would lead you to adopt a different test criterion. What you would look at would not be the ratio of successes obtained, but how long it took him to obtain it. And you would have a very simple test of significance which said if it took you so long to achieve this increase in the score above the chance fraction, this is not at all strong evidence for E.S.P., it is very weak evidence. And the reversing of the choice of test criteria would I think overcome the difficulty.

This is the answer to the point Professor Savage makes; he says why use one method when you have vague knowledge, when you would use a quite different method when you have precise knowledge. It seems to me the answer is that you would use one method when you have precisely determined alternatives, with which you want to compare a given hypothesis, and you use another method when you do not have these alternatives.

SAVAGE: May I digress to say publicly that I learned the stopping-rule principle from Professor Barnard, in conversation in the summer of 1952. Frankly, I then thought it a scandal that anyone in the profession could advance an idea so patently wrong, even as today I can scarcely believe that some people resist an idea so patently right. I am particularly surprised to hear Professor Barnard say today that the stopping rule is irrelevant in certain circumstances only, for the argument he first gave in favour of the principle seems quite unaffected by the distinctions just discussed. The argument then was this: The design of a sequential experiment is, in the last analysis, what the experimenter actually intended to do. His intention is locked up inside his head and cannot be known to those who have to judge the experiment. Never having been comfortable with that argument, I am not advancing it myself. But if Professor Barnard still accepts it, how can he conclude that the stopping-rule principle is only sometimes valid?

BARNARD: If I may reply briefly to Professor Savage's question as to whether I still accept the argument I put to Professor Savage in 1952 (Barnard, 1947a), I would say that I do so in relation to the question then discussed, where it is a matter of choosing from among a number of simple statistical hypotheses. When it is a question of deciding whether an observed result is reasonably consistent or not with a single hypothesis, no simple statistical alternatives being specified, then the argument cannot be applied. I would not claim it as foresight so much as good fortune that on page 664 of the reference given I did imply that the likelihood-ratio argument would apply 'to all questions where the choice lies between a finite number of exclusive alternatives'; it is implicit that the alternatives here must be statistically specified.

SAVAGE: The question of imprecisely determined alternatives is provocative, but in the example of scores on a test for extrasensory perception, it seems to me that the alternatives are quite well specified. If the subject's mean score is not that of the null hypothesis, it is somewhat different, presumably higher. Something like section (*d*) of Dr Smith's contribution should apply, except that account should be taken of the fact that if there is any E.S.P. at all we expect it to be very small from general experience.

A valuable thing brought out by Professor Barnard's comments here and elsewhere is that often we are not only vague as to how our opinion is distributed over the possibilities but even vague as to what the possibilities are.

GOOD: What I call the device of imaginary results is relevant to the previous discussion. Usually we think of an argument from initial or prior probabilities and likelihoods to final probabilities and statistical inference. But if one takes the notion of consistency seriously it is just as legitimate to argue the other way. The words prior and posterior, or initial and final, might mislead one into forgetting this fact.

That is to say you can imagine certain possible final results of an experiment and then use Bayes's theorem in reverse in order to find out what your initial or prior judgements must be for the sake of consistency. For instance, to take a very simple example first, imagine an experiment in E.S.P. in which someone guesses forty consecutive cards correctly, each card having say five possible equally likely forms. You know that the likelihood of that on the null hypothesis, which is that there is no E.S.P. present and that the experiment is carried out honestly and accurately, etc., with no conscious or unconscious cheating, is 5^{-40}. Now if that happened would you or would you not believe that the man had power of extrasensory perception? If you would, then this tells you that the initial probability must exceed 5^{-40} and you have discovered something about your actual state of mind without actually doing the experiment. You merely imagine that this experiment could be performed. Likewise, in this discussion of the stopping rule, suppose you are estimating a probability near a half,

You might imagine that you have done up to say a thousand trials and if that is the sort of thing you had in mind before you started experimenting you will probably be satisfied to use as a distribution when p is not a half, something roughly uniform, though possibly concentrated in a narrow interval covering $p = \frac{1}{2}$. I do not think you can use a uniform distribution going the whole way from $p = 0$ to $p = 1$, if it is a question of the bias of a coin; for example, you might use something uniform in a rather narrow range or something like $p^\alpha (1-p)^\alpha$ to make it smooth. But at the back of your mind you have the idea that you are going to do an experiment of reasonable size. However, if you were told that the experiment might become enormously large, and if you can imagine some possible results of an experiment of that size, you may decide that you would accept E.S.P. even if p were very close to $\frac{1}{2}$. Now if the sigma-age were greater than, say, 10, or something like that, you would have to think awfully carefully. If you were really doing this experiment you would have to think of a great many possible results of the experiment to make sure that you were being consistent; and if you did that, then it may well be that you would decide to use a very curious sharply peaked prior distribution. But I think you might well come round to advance the view that if on tail area probabilities the chance was as small as 10^{-10} this would still not be evidence in favour of E.S.P. But after it really happened, you might begin to doubt your original judgements. So you must try to think out in advance and decide on a prior distribution which would enable you to be consistent whatever happens. That is in theory. It might be very difficult. You do not need more than one test depending on the intentions of the experimenter. In principle you must think of all possibilities and then decide on a single test which will depend on a single prior distribution.

Mr C. B. Winsten: What I was going to say is so closely related to what Dr Good was saying that I hasten to follow him as closely as I can. I, too, want to emphasize that one often may learn about 'initial probabilities' from final probabilities, and I feel this affects the argument quite considerably. Sometimes, as in simple urn experiments, one deduces final probabilities from initial probabilities. On the other hand, one can imagine a situation like that Dr Good has just described in which one has a set of hypotheses which we can call H_1, H_2, H_3, say, and one can suppose a set of observations producing likelihoods, l_1, l_2, l_3. Then one can imagine an observer being given a set of likelihoods, and then being asked which ratio of experimentally obtained likelihoods for hypotheses 2 and 3 he would accept as establishing these hypotheses as having about equal credence, or acceptability, or posterior probability. As a result of this procedure one is establishing the 'prior probabilities', if one can call them that. The content of Bayes's theorem in this situation is, however, completely different from that in the urn case; indeed, it seems to me mistaken even to pose the whole thing as being an application of Bayes's theorem. Instead of saying that the posterior probability is proportional to prior probability times likelihood, one is deducing from the observer's rating of the likelihood scales what weights are needed to establish equal posterior belief.

The term 'weight' is preferable to the term 'probability' because if one is going to use the term probability for something which you obtain from this merging of the likelihood scales, then one must be visualizing carrying out a further experiment later. The numbers one is going to obtain from the weights and the likelihood ratios of the present experiment are then going to be used as weights for the likelihoods of the next experiment. And only in that situation is it in fact worthwhile to try and set up what one might call an analogue of Bayes's theorem. Otherwise it seems to me that one simply tries to discover somebody's degrees of belief from his scaling of the likelihood function. In that situation it seems to me that one should not really even mention Bayes's theorem. One should mention the corresponding formula as a possible summary of the ways in which people treat a summing up of a likelihood choice criterion.

I do not know whether in some situations one could get intermediate cases. I wonder in the light of this whether Professor Barnard's distinction between acceptabilities and probabilities is concerned with whether one can carry out a particular sort of numerical analysis on the choices between likelihoods.

BARNARD: To come back to this point about likelihood and normalization, and in a way back to the general issue, Professor Savage, as I understood him, said earlier that a difference between likelihoods and probabilities was that probabilities would normalize because they integrate to one, whereas likelihoods will not. Now probabilities integrate to one only if all possibilities are taken into account. This requires in its application to the probability of hypotheses that we should be in a position to enumerate all possible hypotheses which might explain a given set of data. Now I think it is just not true that we ever can enumerate all possible hypotheses. We must always leave it open that someone with more imagination, or more knowledge, or more information can come along later and suggest an explanation of the fact with which we are confronted that we just had not thought of at all. If this is so we ought to allow that in addition to the hypotheses that we really consider we should allow something that we had not thought of yet, and of course as soon as we do this we lose the normalizing factor of the probability, and from that point of view probability has no advantage over likelihood. This is my general point, that I think while I agree with a lot of the technical points, I would prefer that this is talked about in terms of likelihood rather than probability. I should like to ask what Professor Savage thinks about that, whether he thinks that the necessity to enumerate hypotheses exhaustively, is important.

SAVAGE: Surely, as you say, we cannot always enumerate hypotheses so completely as we like to think. The list can, however, always be completed by tacking on a catch-all 'something else'. In principle, a person will have probabilities given 'something else' just as he has probabilities given other hypotheses. In practice, the probability of a specified datum given 'something else' is likely to be particularly vague – an unpleasant reality. The probability of 'something else' is also meaningful of course, and usually, though perhaps poorly defined, it is definitely very small. Looking at things this way, I do not find probabilities unnormalizable, certainly not altogether unnormalizable.

Whether probability has an advantage over likelihood seems to me like the question whether volts have an advantage over amperes. The meaninglessness of a norm for likelihood is for me a symptom of the great difference between likelihood and probability. Since you question that symptom, I shall mention one or two others.

First, if we have a probability density of a parameter α, say $\rho(\alpha)$, and reparameterize using, for example, $\beta = \alpha^3$ as the new parameter, then the density of β at the value corresponding to α is $\frac{1}{3}\rho(\alpha)/\alpha^2$. But if $\Pr(x|\alpha)$ is a likelihood in α, the likelihood in β at $\beta = \alpha^3$ is simply $\Pr(x|\alpha)$. Again suppose that x is known to have a Poisson distribution with mean α^{-1} and that $x = 0$ is observed. The likelihood is then $\exp(-\alpha^{-1})$, and it is hard to see how that function, which approaches 1 as $\alpha \to \infty$, could be interpreted as a probability density. The essence of the example is preserved, and the idea of continuous distribution is avoided, if α is assumed to be confined to positive integral values.

On the more general aspect of the enumeration of all possible hypotheses, I certainly agree that the danger of losing serendipity by binding oneself to an over-rigid model is one against which we cannot be too alert. We must not pretend to have enumerated all the hypotheses in some simple and artificial enumeration that actually excludes some of them. The list can however be completed, as I have said, by adding a general 'something else' hypothesis, and this will be quite workable, provided you can tell yourself in good faith that 'something else' is rather improbable. The 'something else' hypothesis does not seem to make it any more meaningful to use likelihood for probability than to use volts for amperes.

Let us consider an example. Offhand, one might think it quite an acceptable scientific question to ask, 'What is the melting point of californium?' Such a question is, in effect, a list of alternatives that pretends to be exhaustive. But, even specifying which isotope of californium is referred to and the pressure at which the melting point is wanted, there are alternatives that the question tends to hide. It is possible that californium sublimates without melting or that it behaves like glass. Who dare say what other alternatives might obtain? An attempt to measure the melting point of californium might, if we are serendipitous, lead to more or less evidence that the concept of melting point is not directly applicable to it. Whether this happens or not, Bayes's theorem will yield a posterior probability distribution for the melting point given that there really is one, based on the corresponding prior conditional probability and on the likelihood of the observed reading of the thermometer as a function of each possible melting point. Neither the prior probability that there is no melting

F

point, nor the likelihood for the observed reading as a function of hypotheses alternative to that of the existence of a melting point enter the calculation. The distinction between likelihood and probability seems clear in this problem, as in any other.

BARNARD: Professor Savage says in effect, 'add at the bottom of the list $H_1, H_2, \ldots$ "something else" '. But what is the probability that a penny comes up heads given the hypothesis 'something else'. We do not know. What one requires for this purpose is not just that there should be some hypotheses, but that they should enable you to compute probabilities for the data, and that requires very well defined hypotheses. For the purpose of applications, I do not think it is enough to consider only the conditional posterior distributions mentioned by Professor Savage.

LINDLEY: I am surprised at what seems to me an obvious red herring that Professor Barnard has drawn across the discussion of hypotheses. I would have thought that when one says this posterior distribution is such and such, all it means is that among the hypotheses that have been suggested the relevant probabilities are such and such; conditionally on the fact that there is nothing new, here is the posterior distribution. If somebody comes along tomorrow with a brilliant new hypotheses, well of course we bring it in.

BARTLETT: But you would be inconsistent because your prior probability would be zero one day and non-zero another.

LINDLEY: No, it is not zero. My prior probability for other hypotheses may be ϵ. All I am saying is that conditionally on the other $1 - \epsilon$, the distribution is as it is.

BARNARD: Yes, but your normalization factor is now determined by ϵ. Of course ϵ may be anything up to 1. Choice of letter has an emotional significance.

LINDLEY: I do not care what it is as long as it is not one.

BARNARD: In that event two things happen. One is that the normalisation has gone west, and hence also this alleged advantage over likelihood. Secondly, you are not in a position to say that the posterior probability which you attach to an hypothesis from an experiment with these unspecified alternatives is in any way comparable with another probability attached to another hypothesis from another experiment with another set of possibly unspecified alternatives. This is the difficulty over likelihood. Likelihood in one class of experiments may not be comparable to likelihood from another class of experiments, because of differences of metric and all sorts of other differences. But I think that you are in exactly the same difficulty with conditional probabilities just because they are conditional on your having thought of a certain set of alternatives. It is not rational in other words. Suppose I come out with a probability of a third that the penny is unbiased, having considered a certain set of alternatives. Now I do another experiment on another penny and I come out of that case with the probability one third that it is unbiased, having considered yet another set of alternatives. There is no reason why I should agree or disagree in my final action or inference in the two cases. I can do one thing in one case and another in another, because they represent conditional probabilities leaving aside possibly different events.

LINDLEY: All probabilities are conditional.

BARNARD: I agree.

LINDLEY: If there are only conditional ones, what is the point at issue?

Professor E. S. PEARSON: I suggest that you start by knowing perfectly well that they are conditional and when you come to the answer you forget about it.

BARNARD: The difficulty is that you are suggesting the use of probability for inference, and this makes us able to compare different sets of evidence. Now you can only compare probabilities on different sets of evidence if those probabilities are conditional on the same set of assumptions. If they are not conditional on the same set of assumptions they are not necessarily in any way comparable.

LINDLEY: Yes, if this probability is a third conditional on that, and if a second probability is a third, conditional on something else, a third still means the same thing. I would be prepared to take my bets at 2 to 1.

BARNARD: Only if you knew that the condition was true, but you do not.

GOOD: Make a conditional bet.

BARNARD: You can make a conditional bet, but that is not what we are aiming at.

WINSTEN: You are making a cross comparison where you do not really want to, if you have got different sets of initial experiments. One does not want to be driven into a situation where one has to say that everything with a probability of a third has an equal degree of credence. I think this is what Professor Barnard has really said.

BARNARD: It seems to me that likelihood would tell you that you lay 2 to 1 in favour of H_1 against H_2, and the conditional probabilities would be exactly the same. Likelihood will not tell you what odds you should lay in favour of H_1 as against the rest of the universe. Probability claims to do that, and it is the only thing that probability can do that likelihood cannot.

SAVAGE: I agree very much with Mr Lindley in this discussion. As I said in my remarks [on p. 80], in so far as I am interested in probabilities conditional on 'not something else', neither the probability of 'something else' nor the probabilities conditional on this hypothesis are relevant. Also, it is not precluded that I should have probabilities given the hypothesis 'something else'; the operational meaning of such probabilities is the same as that of any others, though they are likely to be particularly intuitive as opposed to reasoned.

COX: I wish to make a technical comment on the idea of a simple test of a null hypothesis. Suppose that our simple null hypothesis says that the density of the observations is $f_0(x)$, and that the test consists in calculating the function $t(x)$ and regarding large values of $t(x)$ as evidence against a null hypothesis. Suppose we consider the following family of hypotheses:

$$f_\theta(x) = f_0(x) e^{\theta t(x)} / \int f_0(x) e^{\theta t(x)} dx.$$

That is a family of hypotheses depending on the parameter θ; when $\theta = 0$ it reduces to the null hypothesis. Clearly the uniformly most powerful test of $\theta = 0$ is based on large values of t. Thus the choice of the statistic t is mathematically equivalent to postulating a family of alternative hypotheses. Correspondingly, this general class of alternatives for all t leads to a class of simple tests of significance. So I suggest that the distinction between setting up families of alternatives and using a simple test of significance is primarily a verbal distinction. It may still be important, but there is no working difference between the two in the end; of course the argument cuts both ways.

BARNARD: That would suggest that Daniel Bernoulli was concerned with hypotheses which said that the probability of getting particular configurations of the poles of the planets was some sort of function $e^{\theta\omega}$, where ω is the area of the smallest circle on the sphere which will enclose them all. Now this is clearly not what he had in mind, is it?

SEVERAL SPEAKERS: But it leads to an identical answer.

BARNARD: All he had in mind it seems to me was that if the planets really lie close together, that is something which could probably be explained dynamically, and he very legitimately said, before we start doing this, before we construct alternatives, let us see if we need to. Let us try the simple single hypothesis first. If the data do not fit that, then it is worth while going ahead. If it is consistent with the data let us not waste our time.

PEARSON: But he had a certain kind of alternative in mind. I do not think you need be able to define the hypotheses precisely. You can choose the test without that. If he had in mind the alternative that there was some sort of repulsion, so that the poles would have got as far apart as possible, he would probably have used another kind of test. So the alternatives were affecting the test he used.

BARNARD: Yes, I quite agree with that, but the alternatives which were affecting the test were not statements of probabilistic hypotheses. Therefore I think we in fact agree that significance tests are sensible things to do.

BARTLETT: I think this is a point that Professor Anscombe has made also. If you have rather vague alternatives you can justify classical tests of significance.

WINSTEN: I would like to return to the question of Dr Good's and my remarks. Is measuring prior probability from how different people react to different likelihoods different from proceeding in Professor Savage's way, before the experiment starts?

SAVAGE: It is not different in the sense of referring to different kinds of probability. But it is very valuable to be reminded that if one takes consistency very seriously it is equally legitimate to argue in either direction.

Mr R. SYSKI: I would like to add that the use of the Bayes approach was defended by the Polish mathematician H. Steinhaus as early as 1950. Since then, he and his followers have published several papers dealing with fundamentals and industrial applications (Steinhaus, 1950, 1954; Rajski, 1954, 1958).

On the lighter side of the subject it may be of interest to mention that behind the Iron Curtain Bayes's hypothesis has been mixed up with political implications. Probability Theory as such presents ideological difficulties for communism. See, for example, a curious statement by Gnedenko and Kolmogorov (1954, p. 1), which reads: 'In fact, all epistemologic value of the theory of probability is based on this: that large-scale random phenomena in their collective action create strict, non-random regularity.' Using Bayes's hypothesis, Steinhaus and others overcame this 'official' interpretation, and thus provided possibilities for the unhampered development of Probability Theory.

Finally, I wish to ask how far the theory of Subjective Probability is modified, if at all, when events are specified by abstract valued random variables. There are here several intrinsic difficulties and much depends on the topology of the range space.

SAVAGE: Your final question is a mathematical one rather apart from the main themes of discussion here. To say something about it, de Finetti has always maintained that countable additivity and the attendant restriction of measures to σ-algebras of events are not an essential part of the probability concept. He makes a good case for the idea that probabilities should in principle be thought of as defined for all events. In consequence, many of the mathematical inconveniences of strange range spaces that have been discovered in recent years seem to drop away as side issues.

BARNARD: Can I follow that with a question about de Finetti's attitude to the non-simply additive random distribution on the sphere. I mean Hausdorff's example (Borel, 1926) in which almost the whole sphere is divided into three mutually exclusive sets, A, B and C, such that A is congruent to B (in the sense that a rigid rotation of the sphere will make A coincide with B), and B to C. The extraordinary feature is that the set A is also congruent to the union of B and C. This shows that you cannot have a random distribution on the sphere which is even finitely additive. What does de Finetti say about that?

SAVAGE: I think he would say something like this. Suppose we are trying to make a mathematical model of someone's opinions about where on the earth a certain meteorite is. The person may be so rash as to blurt out that he always regards congruent sets on the surface of a sphere as equally probable. But Hausdorff's example shows that the person's opinions cannot really have this property. In short, a person who had opinions about all sets on the sphere would have to assign unequal probabilities to some pairs of congruent sets.

For my own part, it makes me dizzy to talk about all the subsets of a sphere; that is an awful lot of sets. From a practical point of view, it is enough to know the probabilities of polyhedral sets. Certainly it is more than enough to know the probabilities of all Borel sets. While agreeing with de Finetti that there is no absolute place to draw the line and that no class of sets should be regarded as not having probabilities, I would underline that in practical computations the probabilities of only a relatively few and simple sets are actually used.

GOOD: I think you need to equate probability with exterior measure, if you are going to allow non-measurable sets.

BARNARD: Then you will not have an additive system.

GOOD: That is all right, for measurable sets it comes to the same thing. One is never interested in non-measurable sets in practice.

COX: I would like Professor Savage to elaborate on remarks he made in his paper about the difficulty of justifying randomization from a strict Bayesian point of view. Part of the solution here may lie in attaching a particularly high utility to experiments for which many people can assign a reasonable prior distribution. If one thinks solely of a particular experiment desiring to produce closest possible estimates of a particular difference, then it seems reasonable sometimes not to randomize. One may do what Professor Savage said, namely to think up every little bit of information available and put it all together, and do what seems most likely to produce a precise estimate. But such an experiment may have very little value to anyone else, because not being aware of all the particular technical details, it would not be at all clear that there is not a tremendous systematic error in the experiment. One important property of randomization is that it makes the data reasonably convincing to other people as well as to oneself. Of course this is only half the story; randomization may increase accuracy by removing unsuspected biases. This aspect is particularly important in large experiments where bias is more important than random error.

SAVAGE: I think you lay your finger on the objectives of randomization, to make the experiment useful to others and to guard against one's own subconscious. What remains delicate and tentative for me is to understand when, and to what extent, randomization really can accomplish these objectives.

My doubts were first crystallized in the summer of 1952 by Sir Ronald Fisher. 'What would you do,' I had asked, 'if, drawing a Latin square at random for an experiment, you happened to draw a Knut Vik square?' Sir Ronald said he thought he would draw again and that, ideally, a theory explicitly excluding regular squares should be developed. As I have learned since, other statisticians have had, and worked on, this same idea; see, for example, Jones (1958), Yates (1951a, b). This illustrates once more that one need not be a Bayesian to arrive at criticisms to which the Bayesian is led systematically.

The possibility of accidentally drawing a Knut Vik square or accidentally putting just the junior rabbits into the control group and the senior ones into the experimental group illustrates a flaw in the usual reference-set argument that sees randomization as injecting 'objective', or gambling-device probabilities into the problem of inference. If the randomization and the experiment were so executed by an automaton that no one knew which Latin square had been drawn or which animals had been put in the control group, the argument would, I suppose, apply. But, in fact, this information is not, and ought not to be, kept from the experimenter. And he ought not, in principle, to withhold it from those to whom he communicates his results.

In practice, we may hope, if the experiment is rather large and so designed as to control the variables that (subjectively) look most important, then randomization will almost always lead to a layout that does not look excessively suspicious to any given observer. But this hope needs serious investigation. Perhaps randomization is even one of the most efficient ways to arrive at such widely acceptable layouts. (Such rumours as that artists can make more random-looking designs than random number generators can are a little disquieting to this suggestion.)

In any event, randomization does remove an important possibility of personal interference, for anyone who believes that the randomization did take place according to Hoyle.

Many statisticians agree that an analysis of an experiment ought not be chosen at random. We think it wrong, for example, to break ties at random or to try to escape from the Behrens-Fisher problem by artificially pairing observations. But it has been puzzling to understand why, if random choices can be advantageous in setting up an experiment, they cannot also be advantageous in its analysis. The discussion Dr Cox and I have been giving of randomization seems to lead to an answer to this question. In making an analysis, there is no need to resort to chance to find a compromise analysis that will nearly suit everybody, for each interested person can in principle make for himself the analysis he thinks best. Attempting a compromise can only lose some of the relevant knowledge won by the experiment. Nor can randomization defend against the dangers of subconscious or conscious bias present at the analysis stage.

The arguments against randomized analysis would not apply if the data were too extensive or complex to analyse thoroughly by the individuals concerned. In such a case study of the data might itself become an empirical study based on sampling. Monte Carlo methods might be used. Or one of many possible expensive analyses might be determined in part by randomization in the hope of nearly pleasing everyone.

It seems to me that, whether one is a Bayesian or not, there is still a good deal to clarify about randomization.

BARTLETT: I think this discussion does indicate a certain tendency to compromise both from the Bayesian point of view and from the frequency point of view. On the one hand those who work in terms of a frequency theory avoid certain possible designs because of notions and prior probabilities of what they might contain. On the other hand the fact that the Bayesian would not adopt a perfectly chosen and systematic design, for whatever reasons, seems to represent a certain compromise, in the direction of introducing objective probabilities.

SAVAGE: From my point of view, the exploitation, in personal relations, of the fact that many people coincide in certain judgements is not a compromise. It does of course point up the common sense behind the belief that objective probability is a definable notion.

GOOD: I think the purpose of randomization from the subjectivist point of view is to simplify the analysis by throwing away some of the evidence, deliberately.

SAVAGE: That is a terrible crime, to throw away evidence.

GOOD: But it is evidence which is subjectively judged to be irrelevant. If you had an experiment in which you had to randomize say a thousand objects, say cups of tea, you can never be sure that you had excluded everything that would not be eventually discovered by someone to contain some peculiarities. And your judgement would be the judgement to suppress all these details.

COX: I think Professor Savage's argument leads to what seems to me an acceptable practical conclusion, that randomization is very useful in large and moderate-sized experiments, but is not really very much good in very small single experiments.

WINSTEN: It means also that you should publish the actual design of the Latin square, or whatever it is you chose, so that people can see whether perhaps they have not got a hypothesis of the other sort that they can fill in.

Mr E. D. van REST: I am rather surprised that previous speakers have tended to minimize the importance of randomization. Randomization seems to be useful whenever knowledge is absent, and I think that is in line with all the previous discussion. Professor Savage discussed the example of animals, recognized to be in two classes, senior and junior.

Directly you can recognize the different classes, they are not a subject for randomization. In other words, we experiment over most of those classes of which we have knowledge and randomize where we have no knowledge. Fisher and Professor Savage rejected a regular arrangement which turned out as the result of randomization. That is exactly explainable in the same way; after the randomization has been done a classification has been recognized. The only reason for throwing it away is that it has not been recognized before starting. You use randomization to perform an averaging function, the averaging out of errors, and it is therefore just as legitimate in small experiments as in large experiments, but it is not so effective. It still needs to be done even though it is not so effective.

BARTLETT: This is the point of view of the non-Bayesian, the usual Fisherian approach. Are you suggesting that your comments justify randomization from Professor Savage's point of view?

VAN REST: To me it does not seem to matter which point of view you take.

SAVAGE: Suppose we had, say, thirty fur-bearing animals of which some were junior and some senior, some black and some brown, some fat and some thin, some of one variety and some of another, some born wild and some in captivity, some sluggish and some energetic, and some long-haired and some short-haired. It might be hard to base a convincing assay of a pelt-conditioning vitamin on an experiment with these animals, for every subset of fifteen might well contain nearly all of the animals from one side or another of one of the important dichotomies. The analysis of covariance (or analysis of the experiment as an unbalanced incomplete multifactor experiment) might give some, but not enough, help.

Thus contrary to what I think I was taught, and certainly used to believe, it does not seem possible to base a meaningful experiment on a small heterogeneous group. In particular, the availability of technically valid confidence intervals may not really enable us to make a convincing measurement.

BARNARD: I have often said that I agree with the Bayesian approach in many situations, especially in industrial problems. I would like, however, to comment on the type of Bayesian argument that hinges on the 'smoothness' of the prior distribution. It seems to me very important to recognize just how smooth the distributions sometimes have to be for this approach method to give good results. In the sampling inspection situation mentioned already, one is tempted to assume that the proportion defective has a very smooth prior distribution say of the β type. This is all right very often for deciding what you are going to do on the basis of a given sample, but very much not all right when deciding what size of sample you are going to take or what kind of sampling you are going in for. It may, for example, lead you to underestimate the tremendous advantage of sequential methods as compared with fixed sample size.

GOOD: I should like to mention a topic rather different from the ones we have been discussing previously. What it has in common with them is in showing that philosophy does have something to offer to practical statistics.

The question was raised by Popper of how 'corroboration' should be defined; see, for example, Popper (1959, p. 387). He proposed various desiderata for it, and suggested a formula, with the remark that better formulae may be found. It is a question of assigning a meaning to $C(H:E\,|\,G)$, meaning and pronounced 'the corroboration of H provided by E, given G'. I think Popper missed out a desideratum which narrows down the field of possible interpretations considerably. It is this:

If evidence is considered in two parts, E and F, then the corroboration of H is analytically determined by that provided by E, combined with that provided by F when E is known.

From this axiom, combined with other mild ones, it follows that $C(H:E\,|\,G)$ must be a function $f\{P(H\,|\,EG)-P(H\,|\,G)\}$, where $f(.)$ is a differentiable function.*

Two of the interpretations of $C(H:E\,|\,G)$ are then $I(H:E\,|\,G)$, the

* The detailed analysis has since been published (Good, 1960).

('unexpectated') amount of information concerning H, provided by E, given G, and $W(H:E|G)$, the weight of evidence concerning H provided by E, given G. Symbolically,

$$I(H:E|G) = \log\{P(E|H.G)/P(E|G)\},$$
$$W(H:E|G) = \log\{P(E|H.G)/P(E|\bar{H}.G)\}$$
$$= I(H:E|G) - I(\bar{H}:E|G)$$
$$= \log\{O(H|E.G)/O(H|G)\},$$

where O stands for 'odds', $p/(1-p)$, where p is a probability, and the bar stands for negation.

If corroboration has to be a function of $P(E|H.G)$ and $P(E|\bar{H}.G)$ alone, then it can be proved to be an increasing function of the weight of evidence.

A reasonable aim in the design of an experiment would be the maximization of the expected corroboration, for a given cost in experimentation, where the corroboration is one of the additive kinds, such as information or weight of evidence. Which of these two is more sensible will presumably depend on the narrowness of the intervals within which we can judge the probabilities $P(E|\bar{H}.G)$. Lindley (1956) considered the use of expected amounts of information in the design of experiments; in my book (mentioned above) I implicitly took it for granted that expected weight of evidence was relevant.

In order that these remarks should not be misleading, I should add that I still consider, with Savage, that the basic principle of rational behaviour is the maximization of expected utility. I have not changed my opinion about this since reading a chapter by F. P. Ramsey over twenty years ago. But in applications the emphasis is often on the judgements that can be made with the greatest precision: sometimes this will be the probabilities, and sometimes the utilities, and sometimes a mixture.

Dr G. M. JENKINS:* It is surprising that one of the features which has been accepted without much discussion or disagreement in this symposium is the role played by the likelihood function in statistical

---

* Dr Jenkins was on leave of absence at the time of the meeting and subsequently sent in the following contribution.

theory in so far as it describes the properties of the sample. It is worth noting that some more discussion is required about the choice of the likelihood function as a starting point in any theory of inference.

Main interest has centred around the role played by Bayes's Theorem. Professors Bartlett and Pearson have indicated that they would not use Bayes's Theorem because either they do not recognize its validity or usefulness, or else, even if they were prepared to grant it recognition, choose not to use it. Professors Barnard and Savage and Mr Lindley accept the use and usefulness of Bayes's Theorem, but differ in the extent to which they would apply it. Thus Professor Barnard is prepared to use Bayes's Theorem if the prior distribution is capable of objective description in the sense that past records are available from which some quantitative evaluation may be made, whereas Professor Savage and Mr Lindley are prepared to use it when the prior probabilities involved are far more vague in origin.

I think that ignoring Bayes's Theorem has put much of modern statistics out of gear with scientific thinking; that one indeed very rarely collects observations without some prior probabilities or prior information. In this context, it is necessary to distinguish carefully between prior information in the form of approximate statements such as 'the distribution is normal with given variance', or 'the regression is linear', from prior distributions which are statements about the relative frequencies of a given parameter or set of para- meters derived from previous experience or intuition. Prior informa- tion in the way of an assumption about the model and about the distribution or joint distributions of the errors is of course essential to the writing down of the likelihood function in the first place. Alternatively we may write down likelihood functions which are sufficiently robust with respect to the sort of inference that we are interested in making.

The distinction between the sort of information which should be fed into Bayes's Theorem which marks the difference of approach between Professor Barnard on the one hand and Professor Savage and Mr Lindley on the other is best illustrated by means of an example. In the design of sampling inspection schemes, it is now being accepted that those based on the use of prior distributions (usually referred to as *process curves*) are likely to lead to better results than the purely subjective judgements which had been considered previously. On the other hand there are situations, e.g. when an inspection scheme is being designed for a new product, in which there is no process curve available apart from the few results which are inevitably collected during the process of research and development. In these situations, it would be foolish to ignore the engineering experience of those who developed the product and reasonable guesses about the possible quality of the product may be used in the design of initial schemes which can then be modified in the light of further evidence about the process curve.

What is probably required is a new word to distinguish between prior probabilities of an objective nature and those of a more sub-jective or personal nature. To the latter might be ascribed the word 'hunches', although this is certain to meet with objections from some quarters. What is clear and obvious, however, is the fact that if the information which is fed into Bayes's Theorem is vague and possibly very imprecise, then the corresponding posterior probabilities or expected losses will reflect this imprecision.

Discussion has also been confined entirely to what may be described as *static* theories of inference. All these theories are concerned with statements about sets of statistical parameters which are assumed to be constants of the problem. The notion that one is sampling from finite or infinite populations specified by these 'fixed' parameters is one which has proved useful in the development of statistical theory up to the present. Reflection will perhaps serve to indicate that this is a restrictive assumption and one which may eventually prove to be of limited usefulness in the handling of experimental data.

It is worth noting that Fisher appears at no time to have attached great importance to this concept. Thus in the use of maximum likeli-hood, fiducial inference and more explicitly in the use of conditional inference, Fisher has always thought in terms of the possible values of the parameters which 'flow' from the estimate obtained from the sample. Thus in conditional inference, statements are made using reference sets generated from within the sample which refer only to parameters which are of direct interest in the hypothesis being examined. Thus in applying the conditional argument to the problem of testing for randomness in binary sequences (and more generally about various hypotheses concerning Markov chains), the inference about independence is made conditional on the number of 1's or 0's in the observed sequence. As pointed out by Cox (1958b), there are two advantages to this sort of approach, viz. relevance and expediency. Thus, it is restrictive and unnecessary to assume that we are sampling from a population for which there is a fixed probability P for the occurrence of a 1. All that is required is that the proportion of 1's is not changing violently over the length of the sample. Furthermore, it is expedient to use the conditional approach in problems of a discrete nature such as those raised in inference about Markov chains since it leads to the elimination of all the nuisance parameters not relevant to the hypothesis being examined.

In conditional inference, it is possible to see the germ of what may be described as a *dynamic* theory of inference. By this is meant that the statistical parameters which are effectively regarded as constants in the classical theory are themselves regarded as being governed by a stochastic process (usually of a non-stationary type; if it were stationary then of course the problem could be redefined in terms of new parameters relating to the behaviour of the stationary process) in the dynamic theory. This is clearly more in keeping with the behaviour of empirical investigations than the static theory. Thus the inference problem is regarded as a game of strategy between the statistician and nature in which the quantities that are being estimated are themselves changing in an irregular or unpredicatable manner. As further evidence is obtained, new prior probabilities may be fed back into Bayes's Theorem and new posterior probabilities calculated only to be revised at a future date.

These ideas are implicit in the work of Dr G. E. P. Box and his associates at the Statistical Techniques Research Group at Princeton in connection with the optimisation of the mode of operation of chemical plants by means of the technique known as Evolutionary Operation. It would seem that what is now required is a formulation of these concepts in terms of a dynamic theory of inference which should draw on the existing ideas of the static theories and embody them in a framework in which there is a feed back of information via Bayes's Theorem, i.e. a framework drawing on the theory of servomechanisms.

SAVAGE:* Let me make explicit, and comment on, a number of questions that have been brought up during the discussion.

But what if I don't know my own prior probabilities?

In spite of the over-formal arguments that we should be able to know our own prior probabilities by asking ourselves what bets we would and would not make, we often do not really know them at all well. We are vague about specific probabilities, as Professor Pearson has particularly emphasized, and we may not even think of some important relevant hypotheses let alone assign probabilities to them, as Professor Barnard has emphasized. These imperfections in the theory of personal probability are real and render its conclusions imperfect. We must, therefore, use the theory circumspectly, checking it frequently with common sense. We must also be prepared to find that when the sample is, so to speak, too small, an experiment leaves us in a quandary. Not knowing what to conclude is a reality not to be escaped by adopting any so-called 'exact' theory or rule.

Is Bayesian statistics appropriate to some problems but inappropriate to others?

I have yet to see any statistical procedure that makes a durable appeal and cannot be better understood in terms of personal probabilities than in terms of their denial and, therewith, denial of the applicability of Bayes's theorem. Please understand; I am not saying that we Bayesians have the last word in statistical theory which surely would prove false, but rather that a dualistic view of statistics does not seem called for at the present time, and the Bayesian view does seem to have a good deal to offer for the present.

I no longer believe that there exists some alternative to turn to when the subjective method fails to give a satisfactory answer so that there are two qualitatively different kinds of statistical situations. I used to be cowed by critics who said, with apparent technical justification, that certain popular nonparametric techniques apply in situations where it seems meaningless even to talk of a likelihood function, but I have learned to expect that each of these techniques either has a Bayesian

* Professor Savage was invited to conclude the discussion.

validation or will be found to have only illusory value as a method of inference.

To illustrate the question of an alternative method with the topic of interval estimation, the theory of subjective probability often justifies a rather sharply determined belief that an unknown parameter lies in a given interval, as I explained in the part of my main talk dealing with precise estimation. If circumstances are not favourable, as, for instance, when only one or two degrees of freedom are available for estimating a variance, the theory of subjective probability will not allow us to conclude at all sharply what probability ought to be associated with a given interval. To put it differently, a very crude measurement does not overwhelm the differences to be expected between personal opinions. Formally, however, the theory of confidence intervals (and the theory of fiducal intervals also) does not hesitate to base 95 per cent intervals for a variance on one degree of freedom. To be sure, we all know clearly what a 95 per cent interval for variance based on one degree of freedom is. It is a mechanical process so associating with each sample an interval that, no matter what the actual variance is, the probability that the variance will be covered by the random interval is 95 per cent. As we all know, this does not mean that whenever variance is measured with one degree of freedom you would be willing to bet 19 to 1 after seeing the measurement that the particular confidence interval associated with it includes the true parameter. Imagine, for example, that two Meccans carefully drawn at random differ from each other in height by only 0·01 mm. Would you offer 19 to 1 odds that the standard deviation of the height of Meccans is less than 1·13 mm? That is the 95 per cent upper confidence limit computed from chi-squared with one degree of freedom. No, I think you would not have even enough confidence in that limit to offer odds of 1 to 1. The only use I know for a confidence interval is to have confidence in it. When such confidence is not justifiable, is it not empty to say that the confidence interval procedure solves a problem at which the subjective theory throws up its hands?

What am I supposed to publish?

Sometimes listeners to an exposition of Bayesian statistics get the misimpression that they are being urged to publish their own opinions as their analysis of an empirical study. For example, van Dantzig had the impression on reading my *Foundation of Statistics* (Savage, 1954) that I was urging statisticians to write their own opinions into the scientific publications of their clients. Because of this misconception, van Dantzig (1957) called his review of my book 'Statistical priestcraft'.

Incidentally, I do not ordinarily refer to the relation between the statistician and his client in questions of theoretical statistics, for I regard the separation between statistician and client as an accidental detail of real life that we should try to overcome. If the client had sufficient time, energy, and talent he could be his own statistician, and it seems to me that the first object for theoretical study is such a statistically well endowed investigator. In practice, I conceive that the consulting statistician should, to the best of his ability, lend his mind to his client, or make himself one with his client. There are of course great practical difficulties in bringing about the desired unity and understanding, and the importance of discussing such problems is not to be overlooked, but I have not been discussing them here.

Now, when we Bayesians emphasize that all opinions are but opinion, we do not mean that a scientist publishing the results of his investigation has said the last word when he tells the world what his opinion is. Quite the contrary, the first thing that he ought to tell is what he has observed. In principle, he should do this so well that his peers will know what happened as well as if they had done the experiment themselves. This is in idealization quite unachievable in practice, but approximation to it is the core of a serious research report. In particular, numerical data should be reported as fully as is practical. The most excusable abbreviations are perhaps attempts to condense the data by means of sufficient statistics, but even these are often detrimental, because the sufficient statistics are sufficient only for some model that is nominally accepted, but that might justifiably be rejected in view of some details lost in condensing the data to a sufficient statistic.

Not in principle as an essential but as a courtesy and perhaps as a practical necessity, the scientist may present an opinion that he hopes will be more or less public. His argument would be of the following form, though some parts of it might be left tacit: 'I suppose that you all, like me, will agree on such and such aspects of our prior opinions and on such and such a model of the experiment. According to Bayes's theorem, we now all have approximately such and such opinions in common until one of us has more data on the basis of which to revise opinions.' A simple example occurs implicitly, I think, whenever someone reports that he made, say, five measurements on a heretofore ill-determined physical constant and gives their mean $\bar{x}$ and standard deviation s. No one will have a sharp prior opinion about the constant or the precision of the experimental method, so, if the possibility of bias in the measurements is neglected, everyone concerned should have, and will be content to have, for his posterior distribution nearly a t-distribution on four degrees freedom about $\bar{x}$ and scaled by $s/\sqrt{5}$. (Of course, the possibility of bias is actually of great practical importance in such an experiment, and gives the best of them a tentative quality not often reflected in textbook discussion.)

Finally, and quite incidentally, the investigator may choose to tell his peers some of the things that he feels in his bones without having any public grounds for conviction. This is frequently done, and of course serves some practical purposes, but it is an utter misconception to imagine that Bayesian statistics attaches central theoretical importance to the experimenter's publication of his personal opinion. Rather, we hope he will so publish that each reader can best form his own personal opinion.

How do statistical inferences differ from inferences generally?

Professor Bartlett has stressed that statistical inferences are special and that mathematical theory can be applied to them in a manner that is impossible, or at least unusual, outside of statistics. I concur in this, as I have said in my talk, but Professor Bartlett and I may not be in perfect agreement as to where this difference resides.

As nearly as I can make out, the most characteristic thing about problems in mathematical statistics is the role in each of some specific model, that is, a specific function $\Pr(x|\lambda)$. The model reflects what is taken to be public agreement about the probability of the datum x as a function of the parameter λ. This is the structure even of so-called nonparametric problems.

Though I call such a well-defined public model characteristic, I am not really sure to what extent it is essential to statistical practice and to what extent it is induced by habit or convention. For one thing, in so far as you accept the likelihood principle you will agree that one really needs only the likelihood of x as a function of λ, not probability of x as a function of λ. Still more, since usually no one really takes the model seriously as anything but a tentative approximation, we may some day learn how to express ourselves more accurately and fully.

The public character of practical models sometimes has to do with large numbers and the statistical order that can come out of chaos. But symmetry also can give rise to public agreement, without large numbers.

So far as the preceding remarks are concerned, the problem of inferring something about the bias of a penny from three tosses would seem to be a problem in statistical inference. When the ensign of small-sample statistics flew high, it would hardly have been questioned that this problem or the problem of estimating a variance from one or two degrees of freedom was a statistical problem. But perhaps today some of you will feel with me that problems based on excessively small samples, though they must necessarily merge gradually with those based on adequate samples, do not quite belong to the main line of statistics. At any rate, the problems that I have called precise measurement have an important property that can hardly be overemphasized. For such problems lead, in practice, to posterior opinions that are nearly the same from person to person. In testing problems, there can also be public agreement, but not of quite so subtle a kind as in precise estimation; a test may produce overwhelming practical evidence in favour of, or against, a hypothesis, but it does not leave everybody with nearly the same posterior odds. The precision by means of which some experiments induce practical public agreement also often has its source in the law of large numbers and the like. Perhaps, in the last analysis, there is no other source of such precision, but it seems important to mention that, in principle, a single measurement with an instrument of known high accuracy nearly induces the same normal posterior distribution for everyone.

Science or business? Inference or decision?

Some recent discussions of the foundations of statistics have been complicated by assertions that some statistical theory may be valid for business but not for science, and often confused with that distinction there has been another to the effect that problems of inference are very different from problems of decision.

It does not seem to me that any evidence has ever been brought forward that a statistical theory philosophically sound for practical affairs is inappropriate for science or vice versa. Indeed, it seems unlikely that such a thing should occur at a philosophic level, for many kinds of business considerations can, and properly do, enter the loftiest laboratories – how to allocate the time and money of the laboratory to various problems, for example.

The distinction between inference and decision does seem meaningful to a Bayesian. *Inference* is for us the art of arriving at posterior probabilities; *decision* is concerned directly with action. But, from the Bayesian point of view, the two concepts are not in disharmony with one another. Inference is useful in decision, and the posterior probabilities that figure in inference are, like all probabilities, defined in principle in terms of potential decisions.

What kinds of probability are there?

To me personal, or subjective, probability is the only kind that makes reasonably rigorous sense, and it answers all my needs for a probability concept. So far as this conference is concerned, however, I do not urge so extreme a position on anyone else. If I can leave you thinking that personal probability is interesting and potentially valuable for statistics, my main point will have been made, whether you continue to believe that other concepts of probability are valid or not.

There has been no perceptible defence of the symmetry, or necessary concept of probability here, and I do not really think that concept is tenable. However, as time will show, Sir Harold Jeffreys, a defender of the necessary concept, has made a great and lasting contribution to statistics that has been too little studied.

For some of you, it seems to fly in the face of common sense to deny the existence of frequency probability. But right philosophy sometimes is counter to common sense, and de Finetti has carefully worked out a subjectivistic analysis of the situation in which we ordinarily talk about frequencies, as I have mentioned [on p. 69]. From our point of view, the truth behind the frequency concept of probability is thus a phenomenon clearly explicable in terms of subjective probability. Similarly, we subjectivists believe that personal probability gives good insight into the truth behind the quest for a necessary definition. The capacity to understand, and to take advantage of, other attempts to formulate a probability concept contributes to the evidence, for me, that the subjective theory is on the right track.

References

ANSCOMBE, F. J. (1954), 'Fixed-sample-size analysis of sequential observations', *Biometrics*, **10**, 89–100.

ANSCOMBE, F. J. (1958), 'Rectifying inspection of a continuous output', *J. Amer. statist. Ass.*, **53**, 702–719.

BAHADUR, R. R., and ROBBINS, H. (1950), 'The problem of the greater mean', *Ann. math. Statist.*, **21**, 469–487.

BARNARD, G. A. (1947a), 'A review of *Sequential Analysis* by Abraham Wald,' *J. Amer. statist. Ass.*, **42**, 658–669.

BARNARD, G. A. (1947b), 'The meaning of a significance level', *Biometrika*, **34**, 179–182.

BARTLETT, M. S. (1940), 'The present position of mathematical statistics', *J. R. statist. Soc.*, **103**, 1–29.

BARTLETT, M. S. (1962), *Essays in Probability and Statistics*. London: Methuen.

BEVERIDGE, W. I. B. (1951), *The Art of Scientific Investigation*. London: Heinemann.

BLACKWELL, D. (1947), 'Conditional expectation and unbiased sequential estimation', *Ann. math. Statist.*, **18**, 105–110.

BOREL, E. (1924), 'A propos d'un traité de probabilitiés', 134–146, Note II of *Valeur Pratique et Philosophie des Probabilités*. Paris: Gauthier-Villars (1939). [A review of Keynes's *Treatise*; originally in *Revue Philosophique*, **98** (1924), 321–336.]

BOREL, E. (1926), *Traité du Calcul des Probabilités*, Tome II, Fasc. 1 – Applications á l'Arithmetique. Paris: Gauthier-Villars.

BRIDGMAN, P. W. (1940), 'Science: public or private', *Phil. Sci.*, **7**, 36–48.

CARNAP, R. (1950), *Logical Foundations of Probability*. University of Chicago Press.

CHERNOFF, H., and MOSES, L. E. (1959), *Elementary Decision Theory*. New York: Wiley.

COX, D. R. (1958a), 'Some problems connected with statistical inference', *Ann. math. Statist.*, **29**, 357–372.

COX, D. R. (1958b), 'The regression analysis of binary sequences', *J. R. statist. Soc.* B, **20**, 215–242.

DE FINETTI, B. (1937), 'La prévision: ses lois logiques, ses sources subjectives', *Ann. Inst. H. Poincaré*, **7**, 1–68.

DE FINETTI, B. (1949), 'Sull impostazione assiomatica del calcole delle probabilità', *Annali Triestini*, Ser. 2, **19**, 29–81.

DE FINETTI, B. (1958), 'Foundations of probability', *Philosophy in the Mid-century*, La Nuova Italia Editrice, Florence, 140–147.

DEGROOT, M. H. (1959), 'Unbiased sequential estimation for binomial populations', *Ann. math. Statist.*, **30**, 80–101.

ELVEBACK, L. (1958), 'Actuarial estimation of survivorship in chronic disease', *J. Amer. statist. Ass.*, **53**, 420–440.

FELLER, W. (1940), 'Statistical aspects of E.S.P.', *J. Parapsychol.*, **4**, 271–298.

FIELLER, E. C., CREASY, M. A., and DAVID, S. T. (1954), 'Symposium on interval estimation', *J. R. statist. Soc.* B, **16**, 175–222.

FISHER, R. A. (1915), 'Frequency distribution of the values of the correlation coefficient in samples from an indefinitely large population', *Biometrika*, **10**, 507–521.

FISHER, R. A. (1925), *Statistical Methods for Research Workers*. Edinburgh: Oliver and Boyd.

FISHER, R. A. (1934), 'Two new properties of mathematical likelihood', *Proc. roy. Soc.* A, **144**, 285–307.

FISHER, R. A. (1955), 'Statistical methods and scientific induction', *J. R. statist. Soc.* B, **17**, 69–78.

FISHER, R. A. (1956), *Statistical Methods and Scientific Inference*. Edinburgh: Oliver and Boyd.

FISHER, R. A. (1958), *Smoking and Lung Cancer*. Edinburgh: Oliver and Boyd.

FRY, T. C. (1934), 'A mathematical theory of rational inference (a nonmathematical discussion of Bayes' theorem)', *Scripta Mathematica*, **2**, 205–221.

GIRSHICK, M. A., MOSTELLER, F., and SAVAGE, L. J. (1946), 'Unbiased estimates for certain binomial sampling problems with applications', *Ann. math. Statist.*, **17**, 13–23.

GNEDENKO, B. V., and KOLMOGOROV, A. N. (1954), *Limit Distributions for Sums of Independent Random Variables*. Cambridge, Mass.: Addison-Wesley.

GOOD, I. J. (1950), *Probability and the Weighing of Evidence*. London: Griffin.

GOOD, I. J. (1952), 'Rational decision', *J. R. statist. Soc.* B, **14**, 107–114.

GOOD, I. J. (1960), 'Weight of evidence, corroboration, explanatory power, information and the utility of experiments', *J. R. statist. Soc.* B, **22**, 319–331.

GRUNDY, P. M., and HEALY, M. J. R. (1950), 'Restricted randomiz-ation and quasi-Latin squares', *J. R. statist. Soc.* B, **12**, 286–291.

HEWITT, E., and SAVAGE, L. J. (1955), 'Symmetric measures on Cartesian products', *Trans. Amer. math. Soc.*, **80**, 470–501.

HODGES, J. L., and LEHMANN, E. L. (1952), 'The use of previous experience in reaching statistical decisions', *Ann. math. Statist.*, **23**, 396–407.

JEFFREYS, H. (1948), *Theory of Probability*. Oxford University Press (2nd edition).

JEFFREYS, H. (1957), *Scientific Inference*. Cambridge University Press (2nd edition).

JONES, H. L. (1958), 'Inadmissible samples and confidence limits', *J. Amer. statist. Ass.*, **53**, 482–490.

KAPLAN, E. L., and MEIER, P. (1958), 'Non-parametric estimation from incomplete observations', *J. Amer. statist. Ass.*, **53**, 457–481.

KHINCHIN, A. I. (1949), *Mathematical Foundations of Statistical Mechanics*. New York: Dover.

KOOPMAN, B. O. (1940a), 'The axioms and algebra of intuitive probability', *Ann. Math.*, **41**, 269–292.

KOOPMAN, B. O. (1940b), 'The bases of probability', *Bull. Amer math. Soc.*, **46**, 763–774.

KOOPMAN, B. O. (1941), 'Intuitive probabilities and sequences', *Ann. Math.*, **42**, 169–187.

LEHMANN, E. L. (1958), 'Significance level and power', *Ann. math. Statist.*, **29**, 1167–1176.

LEHMANN, E. L. (1959), *Testing Statistical Hypotheses*. New York: Wiley.

LINDLEY, D. V. (1956), 'On a measure of the information provided by an experiment', *Ann. math. Statist.*, **27**, 986–1005.

LINDLEY, D. V. (1958), 'Professor Hogben's "crisis" – A survey of the foundations of statistics', *Appl. Statist.*, **7**, 186–198.

LINDLEY, D. V. (1961), 'The use of prior probability distributions in statistical inferences and decisions', *Proc. Fourth Berkeley Symposium*, **1**, 453–468.

MOLINA, E. D. (1931), 'Bayes' theorem, an expository presentation', *Bell Tel. System Tech. Publ.*, *Monograph B*, 557.

NEYMAN, J. (1934), 'On the two different aspects of the representative method: the method of stratified sampling and the method of purposive selection', *J. R. statist. Soc.*, **97**, 558–625.

NEYMAN, J., and PEARSON, E. S. (1933), 'The testing of statistical hypotheses in relation to probabilities *a priori*', *Proc. Camb. phil. Soc.*, **29**, 492–510.

PITMAN, E. J. G. (1939), 'The estimation of the location and scale parameters of a continuous population of any given form', *Biometrika*, **30**, 391–421.

POPPER, K. (1959), *The Logic of Scientific Discovery.* London: Hutchinson.

RAJSKI, C. (1954), 'Comparing general populations on the basis of Bayes's rule', *Zastosowania Matematyki*, **1**, 330–341 (Polish with English summary).

RAJSKI, C. (1958), 'The Bayes postulate and entropy', *Zastosowania Matematyki*, **4**, 91–94 (Polish with English summary).

RAMSEY, F. P. (1931), *The Foundations of Mathematics and other Logical Essays.* London: Kegan Paul.

ROBBINS, H. (1952), 'Some aspects of the sequential design of experiments', *Bull. Amer. math. Soc.*, **58**, 527–535.

SAVAGE, L. J. (1947), 'A uniqueness theorem for unbiassed sequential estimation', *Ann. math. Statist.*, **18**, 295–297.

SAVAGE, L. J. (1954), *The Foundations of Statistics.* New York: Wiley.

SCHLAIFER, R. (1959), *Probability and Statistics for Business Decisions.* New York: McGraw-Hill.

SCHRÖDINGER, E. (1944), 'The statistical law in nature', *Nature*, London, **153**, 704–705.

SIMON, H. A. (1953), 'Prediction and hindsight as confirmatory evidence', *Phil. Sci.*, **22**, 227–230.

STEIN, C. (1945), 'A two-sample test for a linear hypothesis whose power is independent of the variance', *Ann. math. Statist.*, **16**, 243–259.

STEINHAUS, H. (1950), 'Quality control by sampling: a plea for Bayes's rule', *Colloquium Mathematicum*, **2**, 98.

STEINHAUS, H. (1954), 'Probability, versimilitude, credibility', *Zastosowania Matematyki*, **1**, 149–172 (Polish with English summary).

VAN DANTZIG, D. (1957), 'Statistical priesthood (Savage on personal probabilities)', *Statistica Neerlandica*, **2**, 1–16.

WALD, A. (1950), *Statistical Decision Functions.* New York: Wiley.

WALLACE, D. L. (1959), 'Conditional confidence level properties', *Ann. math. Statist.*, **30**, 864–876.

WELCH, B. L. (1939), 'On confidence limits and sufficiency with particular reference to parameters of location', *Ann. math. Statist.*, **10**, 58–69.

WHITTLE, P. (1957), 'Curve and periodogram smoothing', *J. R. statist. Soc.* B, **19**, 38–47.

WHITTLE, P. (1958), 'On the smoothing of probability density functions', *J. R. statist. Soc.* B, **20**, 334–343.

YATES, F. (1951a), 'Bases logiques de la planification des expériences', *Ann. Inst. H. Poincaré*, **12**, 97–112.

YATES, F. (1951b), 'Quelques développements modernes dans la planification des expériences', *Ann. Inst. H. Poincaré*, **12**, 113–130.

Name Index

Subject Index